Branding, Graphic and New Media Design

BIS Publishers

British Design 2003

British Design 2003 consists of three volumes:
-Branding, Graphic and New Media Design
-Interior, Retail and Event Design
-Product and Packaging Design

This multi-volume survey of British Design is published
by BIS Publishers in association with The British
Design Initiative, www.britishdesign.co.uk.

B*I*S

BIS Publishers
Herengracht 370-372
1016 CH Amsterdam
T + 31 (0)20 524 75 60
F + 31 (0)20 524 75 57
E bis@bispublishers.nl
www.bispublishers.nl

>

Any overview of British design is only as good as the work that it showcases. *British Design 2003* is the first survey of its kind, offering a cross-section of the most talented design agencies in every sector. Compiled in the first half of 2002, a period in which the industry was recovering from a less-than-soft landing following years of growth, it reflects the determination of British designers to show their creativity, perhaps precisely because the market has been slow. Each of the almost one hundred studios presented here has contributed in its own way to the striking impact of the survey.

In enterprise, creativity is the key to success. Everything else is about keeping the wheels of the business turning. The best entrepreneurs must have the courage and vision to harness creativity, and the ability to choose partners from a wide range of studios and consultancies. Creativity is essential in defining branding strategy, in devising visual identities to accentuate recognition and product knowledge, or helping brands come alive on Internet. It is a vital part of getting products and product improvements into new markets, and equally important in transforming interiors or retail spaces by implementing a corporate identity strategy.

This first British showcase of recent work by designers in every discipline, makes the search for the ideal design partner a bit easier. *British Design 2003* provides an instant impression of each studio's work – an essential reference tool for whenever professional creative input is needed. Judge for yourself: there's creativity here to suit every taste.

Rudolf van Wezel, Publisher, BIS Publishers

"Design clients either want something for nothing OR throw money around in order to satisfy egos OR there are those that actually recognise value – and get it. Coincidently, design agencies either want money for nothing OR hype their fees in order to justify egos OR there are those that actually add value – and get paid for it." *Roger Felton, Managing Director, Felton Communication*

Bread not Bombs

"In a world full of identities and marks, it is becoming increasingly difficult to differentiate through design, that's why creativity is crucial." *Pierre Vermeir, Creative Director, HGV Limited*

"Brand and identity design must be implemented sensitively and cost-effectively across a wide range of different applications so that distinctiveness is maintained in spite of the different purposes and physical constraints."
Chris Ludlow, Senior Partner, Henrion Ludlow Schmidt

"Clients are savvy now, but there's still a lack of understanding of what our design teams can produce with the new technology. Clients often don't realise the potential of mixing the new and traditional channels". *Gordon Druce, New Media Director, Subliminal*

"To say 'New Media' has come of age after the progress of the last few years is like saying The Industrial Revolution had a mild knock-on effect. It's changed everything. It's the way things are." *Glenn Tutssel, Executive Creative Director, Tutssels Enterprise IG*

"A great brand doesn't have to keep justifying itself or substantiating everything. It's mere presence says everything it needs to say." *Neil Svenson, Principal Director, Rufus Leonard*

"The evolution and application of design and creative management techniques is developing along a continuum of sophistication" *Chris Barrington, Director, Blue Goose*

Branding and Graphic Design Contents

New Media Design

Branding and Graphic Design

Alembic Design Consultants Communications design

Management: Jonathan Miller
Contacts: Jonathan Miller and Melanie Camping
Staff: 6
Founded: 1997
Memberships: Design Business Association

1 Hanover Yard
Noel Road
London N1 8YA
t: +44 (0)20 7288 4580/f: +44 (0)20 7288 4581
email: jmiller@alembic.co.uk
www.alembic.co.uk

Company profile

Alembic is an independent design consultancy specialising in clear and effective communications design.

Equally committed to both creativity and client needs, the Alembic approach is characterised by careful distillation of essential information, an emphasis on substance and structure as well as surface; and awareness of project context, timing and cost.

Alembic works on both long-term strategic projects and one-off communications, with clients of all kinds, from small charities to large public companies.

Typical projects include annual reports and other corporate literature, environmental graphics, marketing communications and on-screen design. Alembic has considerable experience of creating new visual identities for corporate and consumer brands, and develops strategies to evolve, implement and manage existing identities.

Clients

Aberdeen Asset Management
Ceema Technology
CS Healthcare
Datamonitor
Eurosport
Fletcher Priest Architects
Financial Publishing International
First Islamic Investment Bank
Granada Media
Merrill Lynch Europe
Petrogal
Portugal Telecom
Tindall Riley

1   2   3   4

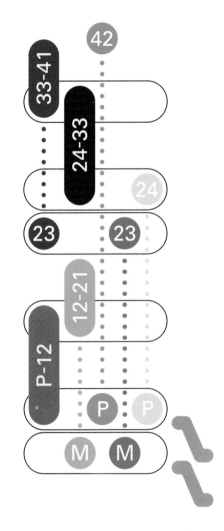

1, 4, 9. Marketing communications for Granada Media
2. Annual report for First Islamic Investment Bank
5, 10. Wayfinding system for Tower 42 (formerly the NatWest Tower)
6. Website for The Sure Group
7. Annual report for Datamonitor plc
8. Corporate fundraising brochure
11. Corporate identity for billiard table manufacturer Hamilton
12. Corporate identity for The Film Editors
13. Corporate identity for picture research agency

5

6

Sure Total Marketing

We are a full service marketing organisation with special skills in marketing. We work with client organisations at all descriptions in successful long-term relationships which

7

8

9

12

13

11

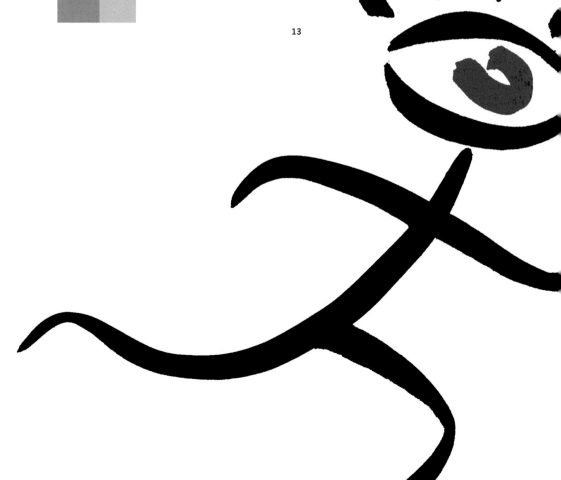

August
Editorial design and publishing

Management: Stephen Coates, Nick Barley
Contacts: Nick Barley
Staff: 7
Founded: 1998

AugustMedia:
116-120 Golden Lane
London EC1Y OTL
t: +44 (0)20 7689 4400/f: +44 (0)20 7689 4401
email: nbarley@augustmedia.co.uk
www.augustmedia.co.uk

Formed in 1998 by award-winning creative director
Stephen Coates and publisher Nick Barley, August was
set up in the belief that great design requires clear
editorial thinking as well as brilliant art direction. The
unique combination of a design consultancy and a
publishing imprint had enabled August to become one
of Britain's leading specialists in editorial design, with a
particular emphasis on magazines, books, information
graphics, corporate identity, promotional literature and
exhibition design.

August's fast-growing publishing list includes highly
acclaimed titles on architecture, design, urbanism and
contemporary art, as well as a series of books written,
designed, published and distributed in partnership with
other organisations.

Clients include
British Film Institute
Reed Business Information
Emap
Spafax Airline Network
Agnews Gallery
Arts Council of England
British Council
Hayward Gallery
Institute of Contemporary Arts
London Arts
Tate
Victoria & Albert Museum
Glasgow 1999
Birkhäuser Publishers for Architecture
Booth Clibborn Editions
Faber and Faber
Laurence King Publishing
Phaidon Press
MACS Shipping
BBC
Channel 5
Modus Publicity

1. *Sight and Sound*, art direction of a monthly film magazine,
1998–present. Designed by Anne Odling-Smee and Chris Brawn.
2. *100 Objects to Represent the World*, opera libretto.
3. *Flying over Water*, exhibition catalogue.
4. *Sight and Sound Reader*, cover designs for a book series.
5. *Reading Things*, book design.
6. *Tate Britain, Tate Modern*, gallery guide books.
7. *Tate*, art direction of a tri-monthly art magazine, 1996–2002.
Designed by Stephen Coates and Anne Odling-Smee.
8. *Eye* magazine, art direction of a quarterly review of graphic
design 1990–97. Designed by Stephen Coates.
9. *New Scientist*, redesign of a weekly science magazine.
Designed by Stephen Coates and Ben Acornley.

Overleaf: All titles designed and published by August or
August/Birkhäuser, except *Collaborations*, designed by Peter
Willberg, and *Design Noir*, designed by Alex Rich.

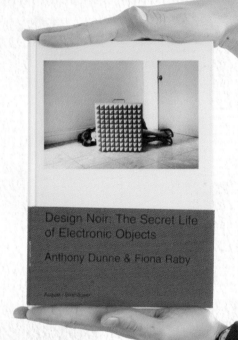

BDP Design

Management: *Martin Cook*
Contacts: *Stephen Anderson*
Staff: *20*
Founded: *1972*

16 Gresse Street
London W1A 4WD
t: +44 (0)20 7462 8000/f: +44 (0)20 7462 6349
email: sc-anderson@bdp.co.uk
www.bdpdesign.co.uk

BDP Design are a multi-discipline design group with
expertise in all aspects of communication design. Our
designers have a recognised expertise in producing
2-D and 3-D design solutions for all types of projects:
environmental graphics, brand development, print
design, website design, interactive presentations,
visualisation and photography.

Our strength lies in the overlap of these creative
disciplines enabling us to deal with a diverse range
of projects.

We operate across the UK and Europe through offices
in London, Manchester, Belfast and Grenoble, France.

See also volume Interior, Retail and Event Design p. 8

"Ideas won't keep:
something has to be done
about them"

ALFRED NORTH WHITEHEAD

Ideas

BDP

BDP Design

Blair
Exhibition design

Management: Bill Lanisek, Rob Edwards, Neil Elliot
Contacts: Bill Lanisek, Rob Edwards
Staff: 9
Founded: 2001

12 St James's Square
London SW1Y 4RB
t: +44 (0)20 7849 5510/f: +44 (0)20 7849 5520
email: contact@blairinc.co.uk
www.blairinc.co.uk

We are a design consultancy specialising in the
creation and execution of exhibitions for corporate
clients attending trade shows and brand owners
requiring representation at public exhibitions.

The heart of our proposition for business, is the
belief that exhibitions are a combination of two critical
elements – the creative and the tactical.

In creative, we consider those aspects of a successful
exhibition that ensure the appropriate application
of design and its impact on fulfilment, as much as
those aesthetic attributes that can mean so much to
highlighting competitive advantage.

Turning the concept into reality and fulfilling the
promise made by a creative proposal is where our
expertise in the management of project detail shines.
This awareness allows us to blend seamlessly the
many elements inherent in effective tactical fulfilment.

We are passionate about design and believe we can
best serve client requirement by presenting the most
relevant and innovative solutions possible, for us this is
a key element in establishing a sustained relationship
with clients.

We are also an innovative organisation in the way
we seek to manage the relationship between project
information and partners throughout the project
lifecycle; we do this by including project partners in
the earliest stages of dialogue.

Our belief in mutuality and the transparent sharing of
information means barriers to fulfilment are removed,
resulting in a more productive and efficient experience.
Whether client, agent or third party supplier, we are all
project partners sharing a mutual desire for the right
result.

See also volume Interior, Retail and Event Design p. 10

Blair Inc Ltd
12 St James's Square
London SW1Y 4RB

t +44 (0)20 7849 5510
f +44 (0)20 7849 5520
e contact@blairinc.co.uk
w www.blairinc.co.uk

blair design exhibitions

**bluegoose
Design &
Branding**

Management: *Chris Barrington, Paul McManus*
Contacts: *Chris Barrington*
Staff: *10*
Founded: *1996*
Memberships: *DBA*

12

Old Council Chamber
90 High Street
Harrow on the Hill
London HA1 3LP
t: +44 (0)20 8869 8500/f: +44 (0)20 8869 8501
email: thinking@bluegoose.co.uk
www.bluegoose.co.uk

bluegoose is a visual communications consultancy
specialising in ideas-led solutions across design
strategy, corporate identity, branding, company
literature and website design. We believe it's the
thinking behind your communications that makes
them relevant and effective. Intelligent creativity can
add real value to your business and a strong design
strategy supports your marketing activities.

We use design and creativity to:

o Differentiate our clients' products and services;
o Develop and manage corporate and brand identity
  systems;
o Enhance external and internal communications
  programmes.

bluegoose is for any organisation more interested in
designing their future, than in watching it happen.

Clients: Ernst & Young, First Quench,
PricewaterhouseCoopers, Legal & General, City of
London Police, The Law Society, Fulham Football Club.

1. Exhibition Gallery, Law Society
2. Corporate Communications, SmytheDorwardLambert
3. Internal Communications, Legal & General
4. Sponsorship Literature, BAR Formula One
5. Change Management, First Quench
6. Service Line Literature, PricewaterhouseCoopers
7. Corporate Hospitality Environment, Rugby Football Union
8. Merchandise Catalogue, Fulham Football Club

Corporate Edge

Management: Chris Wood, Simon Lake,
Bridget Ruffell
Contact: Peter Shaw
Staff: 130
Founded: 1997
Memberships: D&AD, DBA, CIM

149 Hammersmith Road
London W14 0QL
t: +44 (0)20 7855 5775/f: +44 (0)20 7855 5850
email: p.shaw@corporateedge.com
www.corporateedge.com

Corporate Edge is the UK's largest independent
branding and design consultancy, formed in 1997
through a merger of two of the UK's pioneering
marketing services companies: brand consultancy CLK
and design consultancy Michael Peters Ltd. Offering
a unique breadth and depth of branding and design
skills Corporate Edge works in all sectors creating and
evolving product, service and corporate brands - our
skills include futures, research, strategy, naming,
design, corporate literature, new media, interiors and
architecture.

Clients
Anchor
BBC
BG Group
CGNU
COI
Cadbury Schweppes
Champneys
Clubhaus
Daiwa Securities Trust and Banking
Ericsson
Gist
GlaxoSmithKline
GUS
Guinness
ICI
Inland Revenue
Lifeboats
London Development Agency
Met Office
Nestlé
Pearson
Reed Elsevier
Rentokil Initial
Shell
Stax Leisure
Tesco
UDV
Wagamama
Williams F1
The Work Foundation

See also volume Product and Packaging Design p. 34
See also volume Interior, Retail and Event Design p. 22

1. The new identity created by Corporate Edge for The
Industrial Society, which rebranded as The Work Foundation
in April 2002
2. Images from the ICI annual report 2002, created by
Corporate Edge

REALISING THE POTENTIAL OF CORPORATE BRANDS

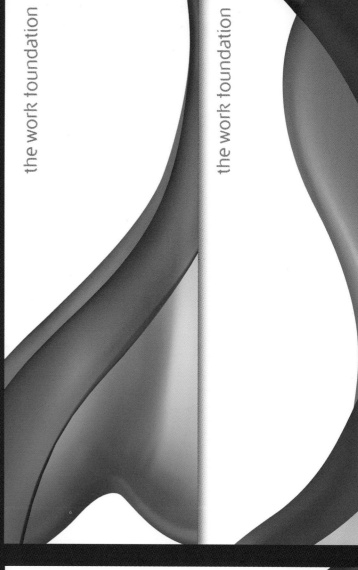

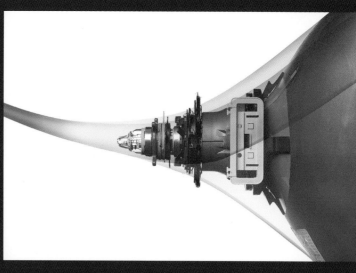

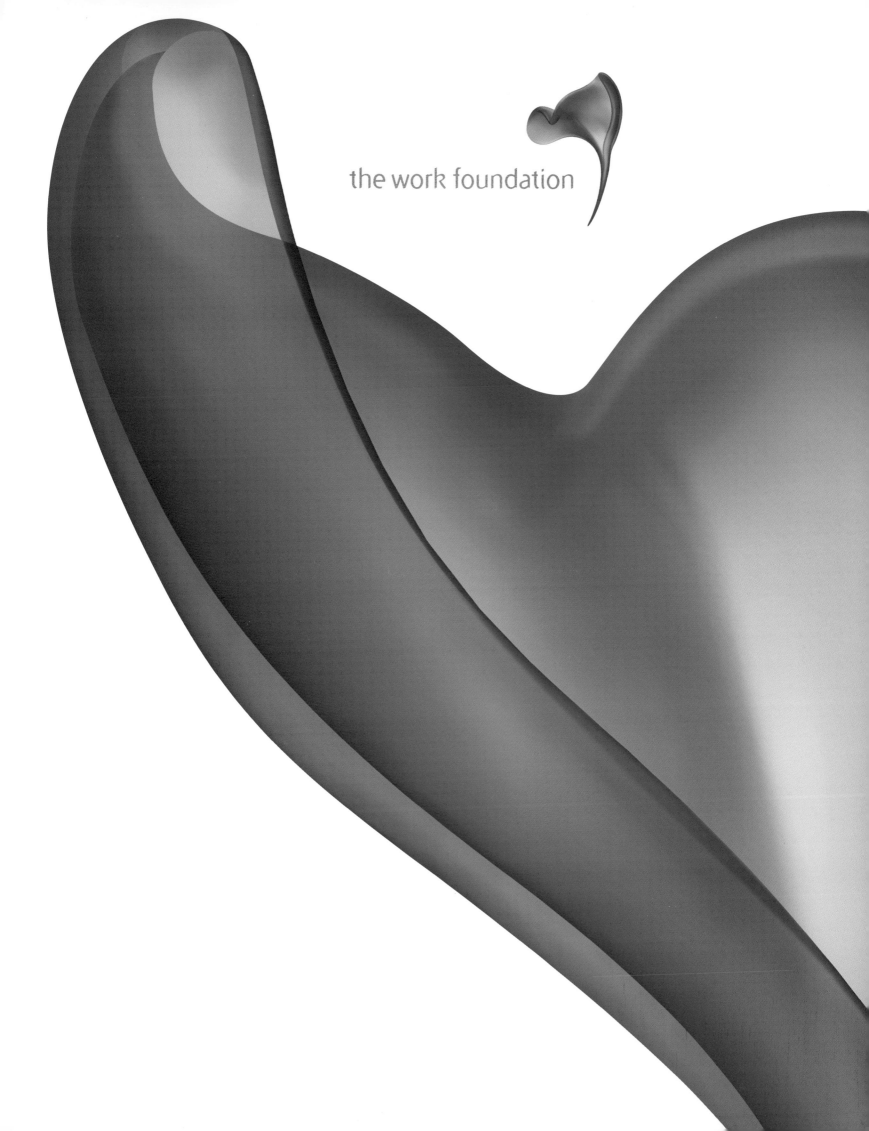

the work foundation

MAKING BRAND COMMUNICATIONS
INCISIVE AND IRRESISTIBLE

The Design Agency

Contacts: Gary Robinson
Founded: 1984

3G1 The Leathermarket
Weston Street
London SE1 3ER
t: +44 (0)20 7407 1797/f: +44 (0)20 7407 1798
m: +44 (0)7711 047446
email: design.agency@easynet.co.uk

The Design Agency, formed in 1984, has successfully handled design and communications projects across a broad spectrum of markets and sectors. Throughout this period our commitment to service and our ability to generate innovative creative solutions has led to the development of many long-standing client relationships.

Our main areas of expertise include:
Annual Report & Accounts
Corporate and Financial Advertising
Corporate Literature
Product Literature
Branding

20

Design Bridge
Corporate and
Service Branding

Management: Sir William Goodenough,
Sophie Severeo, Stefan Butler, Helen Slater, Jon Gold
Contacts: Jon Gold
Staff: 20
Founded: 2000

London office
18 Clerkenwell Close
London EC1R 0QN
t: +44 (0)20 7814 9922/f: +44 (0)20 7814 9024
email: jon.gold@designbridge.co.uk
www.designbridge.co.uk

Amsterdam office
Keizersgracht 424
1016 GC Amsterdam
Netherlands
t: +31 (0)20 520 6030/f: +31 (0)20 520 6059
email: marian@designbridge.nl
www.designbridge.co.uk

At Design Bridge we believe that brands are like
people. They come in all shapes and sizes, from the
well-adjusted to those with more deep-rooted
problems and still more just waiting to be born.
Whatever the scenario, we speak their language and
understand their needs. The common thread is
always fresh thinking, with every brief a new challenge.

Our particular strategic and creative skills can be used
individually, or in combination, to unlock the potential
in every brand. Whether the most compelling need is
for a new corporate or brand identity, promotional
literature, a three-dimensional expression of a brand,
bespoke bottle or graphic packaging, or even a digital
media campaign, we have over 15 years' experience
helping companies around the world to realise their
goals, and those of their product or service brands.

How do you communicate the personality and culture
of a business or organisation? How do you make sure
your customers understand the services you offer
when there is no tangible product? How can you
get your message heard in a sea of branded
communication? We have resolved these issues for
many clients - both B2C and B2B.

See also section New Media Design p. 114
See also volume Product and Packaging Design p. 36

1. Connexxion: new name, identity and design system for Dutch
transport merger
2. Spring: real standout for new global mail business, a joint
venture between TPG, Singapore Post and Consignia
3. UEFA Champions League: 10 years' on, an identity which still
stands for the best in European football
4. Esure: an iconic identity for Halifax/Royal Bank of Scotland
start-up Esure has since driven a national ad campaign
5. Golden Arch Hotels: creating a hotel brand for McDonald's
which stands for internationalism and convenience

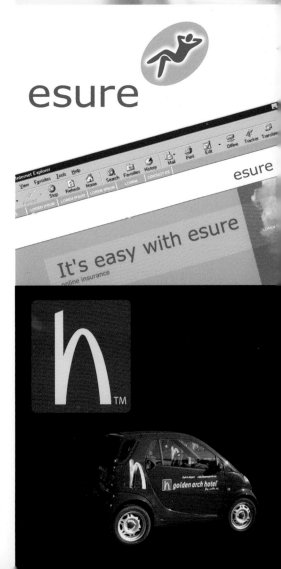

108 PURMEREND
WEIDEVENNE

connexxion

9091 connexxion

DESIGN BRIDGE

Design Research Unit
Signing and wayfinding design

Management: *Paul Cook, Irvin A Morris, Maurice Green*
Contacts: *Paul Cook RIBA*
Staff: *20*
Founded: *1943*
Memberships: *RIBA, BSI, SDS, CSD, BDI, BCB*

The Old School
Exton Street
London SE1 8UE
t: +44 (0)20 7633 9711/f: +44 (0)20 7261 0333
email: info@dru.co.uk
www.dru.co.uk

2103 Universal Trade Centre:
Arbuthnot Road 3
Central Hong Kong
Hong Kong S. A. R
t: +852 2377 4737/f: +852 2736 6457

Company profile

Design Research Unit was founded in 1943 by the celebrated designers Milner Grey and Sir Misha Black. The company's well known core values of design excellence reliant upon sound research, implemented by a multi-skilled, multi-disciplined 'unit', soon became a benchmark in British design. These principles remain in operation today at DRU's offices in London and Hong Kong. Design services provided include architecture, landscape architecture and urban planning, visual communication, signing and wayfinding, and interior design.

Signing and wayfinding

Design Research Unit has a long-standing expertise in corporate communications, stretching back forty years to the design of the well known identity for British Rail [1]. DRU's current commissions involving information design require specific skills to address issues such as clarity, legibility, linguistic requirements and site identity.

In addition to these graphic skills, DRU's architects have been involved in the planning of numerous transport systems worldwide. Understanding of strategic network planning, legislation, planning regulations and most importantly, pedestrian flow is crucial for such projects.

As one cohesive unit, Design Research Unit brings these skills together, creating an unparalleled level of signing and wayfinding expertise. Our client list in this field includes major corporate and public organisations.

A current commission from Railtrack plc involves undertaking a strategic review of wayfinding at all major stations throughout the UK. The design process involves a spatial audit, followed by the production of comprehensive signing schedules and the design of customer information maps.

1. British Rail identity, British Rail, 1965.
2, 4, 10. Railtrack Major Stations signing and wayfinding, Railtrack plc, 2001.
3. Delhi Metro System Map by Finn Butler, DMRC, 2002.
5. Nelson Mandela unveiling the Jubilee Walkway panels, JWT, 1996.
6. Initial passenger flow sketch, Railtrack plc, 2001.
7, 8. Customer information maps, Railtrack plc, 2001.
9. Lea Valley wayfinding signs, LVRPA, 1999.

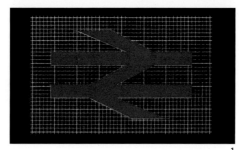

1

2

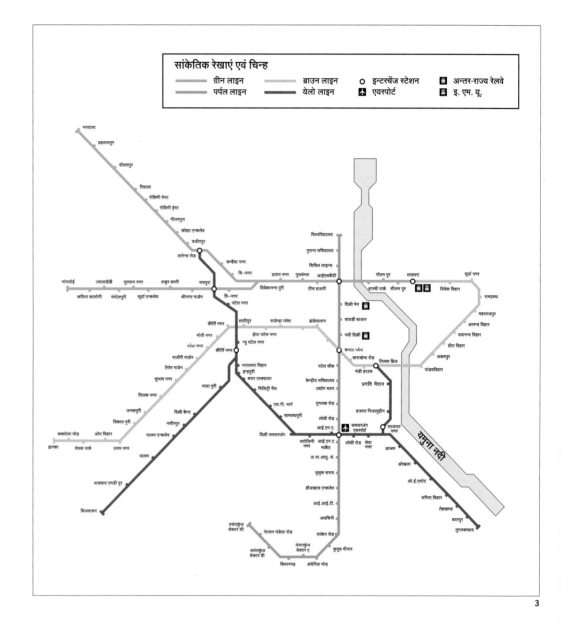

3

4

5

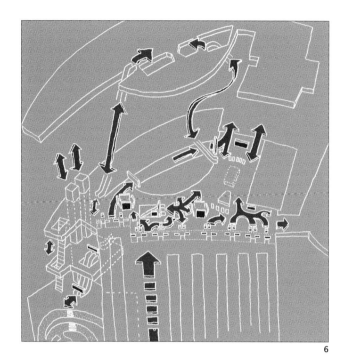

6

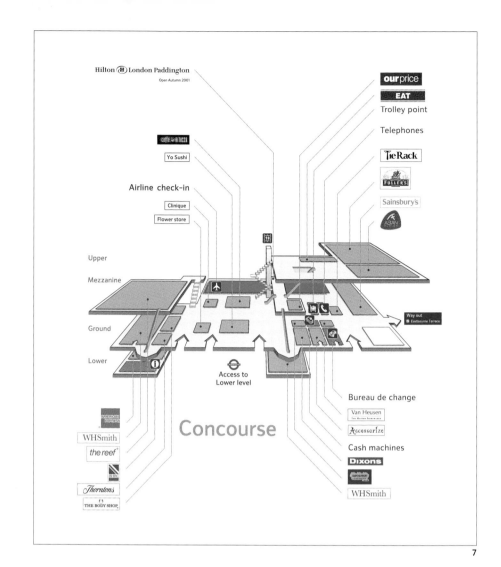

7

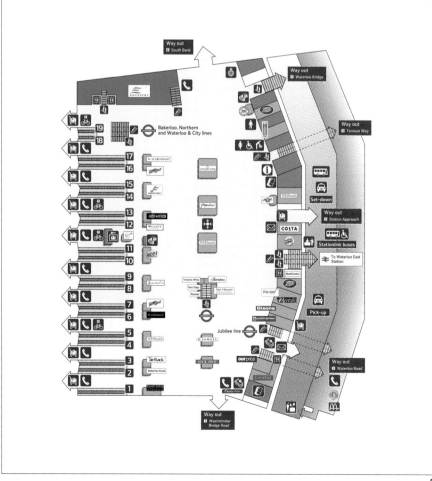

8

9

10

Felton
Communication
Graphic Design

Management: Roger Felton FCSD and Kate Hall
Contacts: Roger Felton or Jennifer Jackson
Staff: 14
Founded: 1989

London Office:
2 Bleeding Heart Yard
London EC1N 8SJ
t: +44 (0)20 7405 0900/f: +44 (0)20 7430 1550
email: design@felton.co.uk
www.feltoncom.com

Company profile

For over 12 years, FELTONs has successfully created, built and managed over 80 brand identities.

Our client base is enviably loyal and intentionally varied - from a City law firm to Europe's largest HIV charity, and a global automotive components manufacturer to a London local government authority.

Our multi-disciplinary culture coupled with our long-term specialist partners has resulted in considerable experience across a broad range of creative applications.

Though our core strengths remain in all forms of design for print and digital media, we regularly undertake more unusual projects. From refuse truck livery and sexual health advertising to conferences and corporate gifts, all are within our visual identity remit.

Our core principles are to differentiate our clients within their respective sectors and deliver highly creative yet effective solutions.

Clients include

ArvinMeritor - Automotive components manufacturer
BAA - UK airport operator
Eucid - Business Intelligence consultants
Field Fisher Waterhouse - City law firm
Galacroft - Hardwood Flooring retailer
Gazeley - Property Developer
Hatfield House - Stately Home
Lambeth Council - London Local Government Authority
NOP - Market Research agency
Pfannenberg - Industrial Cooling supplier
Press Complaints Commission - UK body
SPSS MR - Market Research technologies company
Threshold - Housing Association
Terrence Higgins Trust - HIV and AIDS charity
TMA - Cultural Training consultants
Yarrow - Learning Disabilities charity
White Door - Creative recruitments agents

Image form FELTONs' self-promotional calendar. 'Be Different'.
Photograph by Sam Scott-Hunter

FELTON©

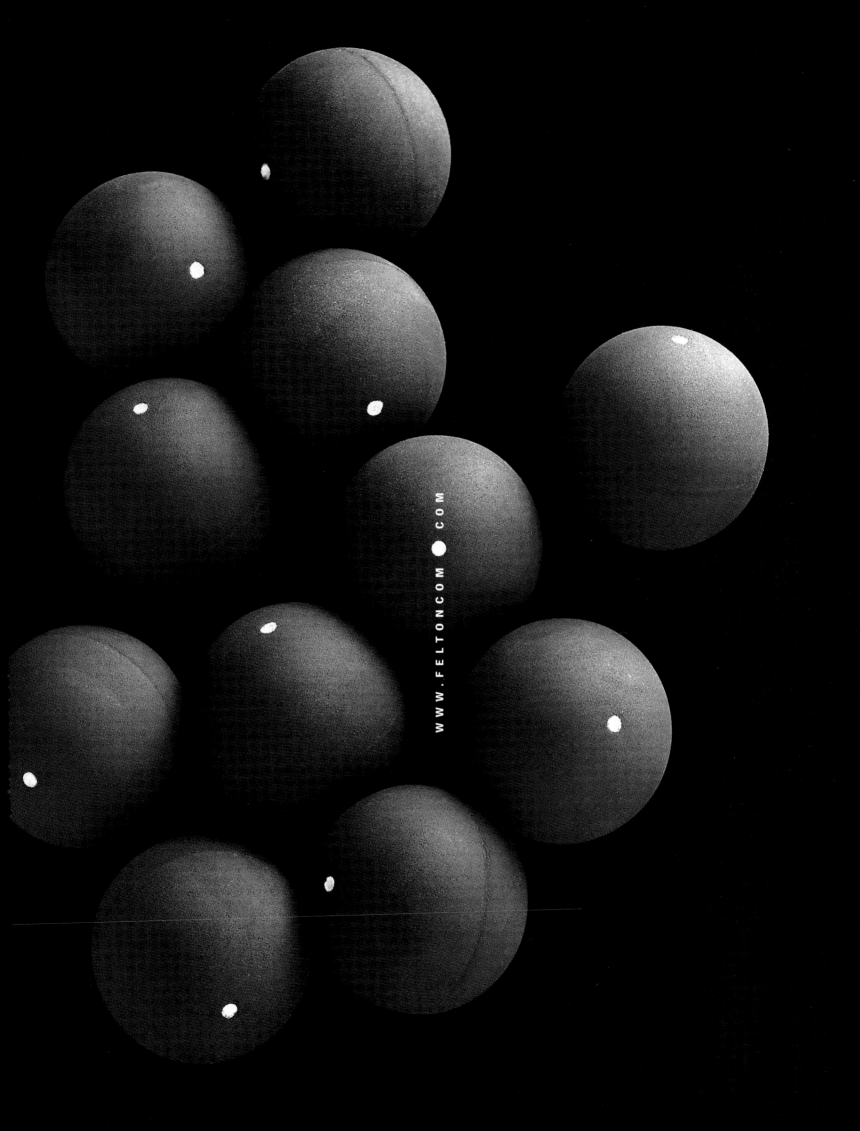

WWW.FELTONCOM●COM

Field Design Consultants Ltd.

Management: Alan Binding, Nigel Roberts
Contacts: Olivia FitzGerald
Staff: 9
Founded: 1993
Memberships: DBA

13 Tottenham Mews
London W1T 4AQ
t: +44 (0)20 7580 1485/f: +44 (0)20 7580 1455
m: 07980 261 348
email: livie@fielddesign.com
www.fielddesign.com

Company Profile

Field. Alan. Nigel. Natalie. Sarah. John. Sam. Livie.
Rosh. Fiona. Designers. Creative. Contemporary.
Experienced. Enthusiastic. Friendly. Brilliant.

Clients

Bromley-by-Bow Community Centre
Cabinet Office
Department of Trade and Industry
Filter Theatre Company
Harvill Press
Heal & Son Ltd
Levi Strauss
MTV
Sci-Fi Channel
The Studio Channel
Virgin Atlantic Airways
Virgin Megastores
Virgin Space

1.

2.

6.

7.
8.

1. European store campaign, Levi's All-Duty Range
2. British store campaign, Levi's All-Duty Range
3. Economy meal service refresh, Virgin Atlantic Airways
4. Corporate identity, Bromley by Bow Community Centre
5. "Sources of Cool" market research study, MTV Networks Europe
6. Seasonal sales promotion cards, Heal & Son
7. Corporate identity, Virgin Space internet cafes
8. Corporate identity, Filter Theatre Company
9. New brand store signage package, Virgin Megastores
10. Gift vouchers, Virgin Megastores

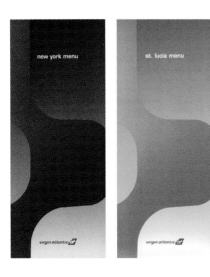

new york menu

st. lucia menu

barbados menu

washington menu

virgin atlantic

virgin atlantic

virgin atlantic

virgin atlantic

bromley by bow centre

decks

£10
ten pounds

£10
ten pounds
ten pounds
ten pounds
ten pounds

05950023

DATE SOLD
TOTAL SALE
RECEIPT NO.
INITIALS

05950023

virgin megastores® gift voucher

Virgin megastores

The Formation Creative Consultants Ltd

Management: Adrian Kilby
Contacts: Adrian Kilby
Staff: 9
Founded: 1994
Memberships: STD

59 Charlotte Road
London EC2A 3QW
t: +44 (0)20 7739 8198/f: +44 (0)20 7729 1950
m: +44 (0)7887 752 684
email: creative@theformation-cc.co.uk
www.theformation-cc.co.uk

The Formation first took to the skies on 1 August 1994 under the command of Adrian Kilby - designer and reincarnated fighter pilot!

We describe ourselves as creative consultants and specialise in brand building. Our experience spans corporate identity, design for print, retail/exhibition design and packaging. We also have a portfolio of advertising work, undertaken on behalf of our clients.

Our approach is personal and respectful, yet thorough and stimulating. We challenge our clients in the same way we expect to be challenged ourselves.

We are responsible for the building of two official 'Millennium Brands' (Pret A Manger and Coffee Republic). Our work is regularly selected for publication and the company has won awards both in the UK and overseas.

1. Pret A Manger: Branding, store design, packaging and graphics.
2. Bagelmania: Branding, store design, packaging and graphics.
3. & 5. New York Nail Company: Branding, store design, packaging and graphics.
4. First Choice Coffee/Grand Cafe: Branding, packaging and literature.

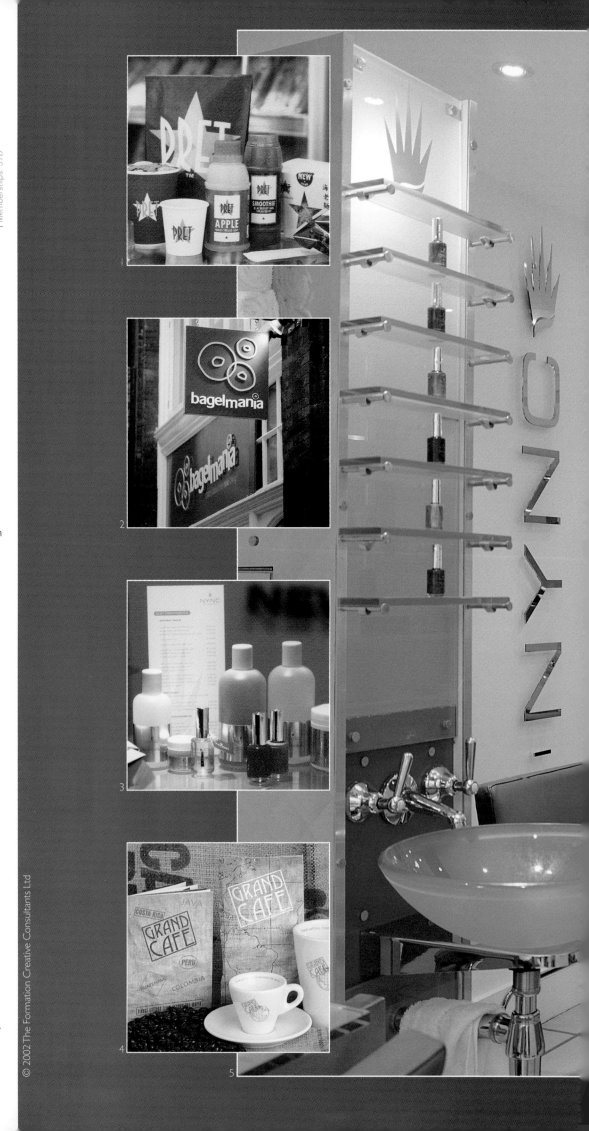

Shellys

COFFEE REPUBLIC

Second World Summit
on Television for
Children

Virgin **direct**
personal financial service

**TYNEDALE
RETAIL PARK**
Discover the Difference

coffee
HOVSE

Henrion Ludlow Schmidt
Branding and wayfinding design

Management: Klaus Schmidt
Contacts: Anthony Ryman
Staff: 35
Founded: 1981
Memberships: CSD

12 Hobart PLace
London SW1W OHH
t: +44 (0)20 7245 4600/f: +44 (0)20 7245 4601
email: info@henrion.com
www.henrion.co.uk

Rothenbaumchaussee 7
D-20148 Hamburg
t: +49 (0)40 4419 530/f: +49 (0)40 4419 5329
email: info@henrion.de
www.henrion.de

company profile
Henrion Ludlow Schmidt is a multi-disciplinary brand
identity consultancy. Our offer includes strategic
positioning, name and identity structures, internal and
marketing communications, and corporate design. We
specialise in complex wayfinding programmes - as
illustrated here.

Selected clients
Amersham International
BAA
Bluewater Park
British Midland Airways
Building Design Partnership
CMS
Commerzbank
DaimlerChrysler
Deutsche Bank
Deutsche Telekom
E-Plus
Flughafen Hannover
Heathrow Express
KLM Royal Dutch Airlines
Krups
London Electricity
London Underground
Mitsubishi Motors
Millennium Dome (NMEC)
Roche Diagnostics
Schott
Tate & Lyle
Transport for London
Vantico
West LB

From left to right: BAA - wayfinding consultancy,
London Underground - sign system, Millennium
Dome - sign design and planning, South Bank
London - identification and wayfinding.

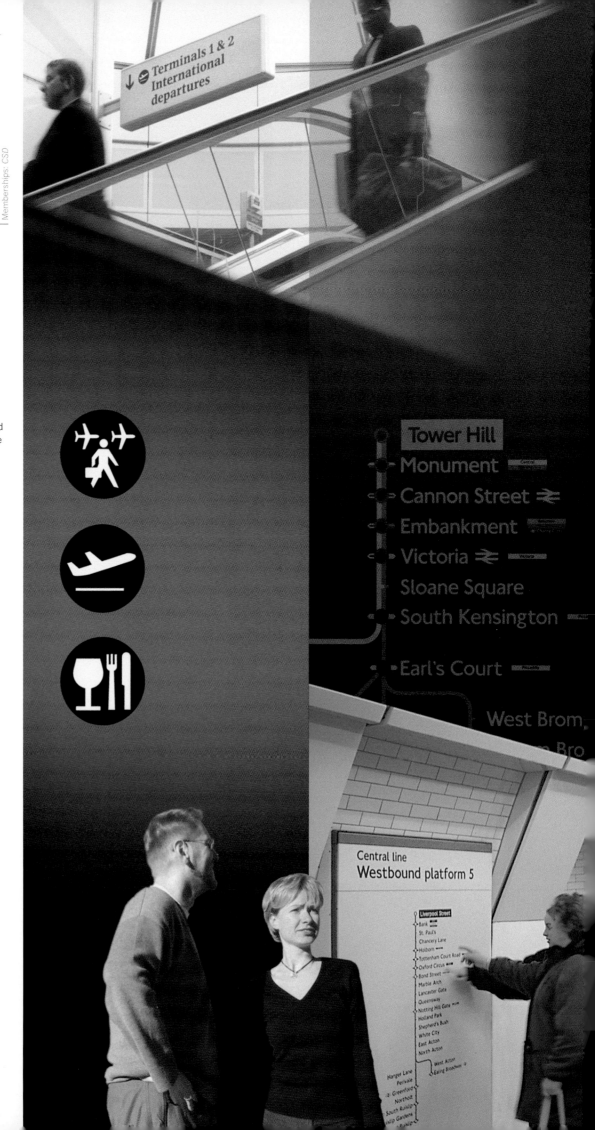

Skyscape
The Round
The Dome
Millennium Pier

Riverside
Sch

Waterloo Stations ≠ ⊖
Royal National Theatre
Museum of the Moving Image
Hall & Hayward Gallery

Cottesloe Theatre

London Television Centre

Oxo Tower & Bankside

HGV

Management: Pierre Vermeir and Barbara Brown
Contacts: As above
Staff: 10
Founded: 1988
Memberships: D&AD, DBA

46a Rosebery Avenue
london EC1R 4RP
t: 020 7278 4449/f: 020 7837 4666
email: design@hgv.co.uk
www.hgv.co.uk

Founded in 1988, HGV is dedicated to producing effective design solutions which communicate on an intellectual and emotional level with impact and clarity.

We believe design is about communication not decoration, and combine our commitment to quality with a clear understanding of the attitudes and information needs of those internal and external audiences who influence our clients' success.

1

1. Identity for upmarket pet shop including logotype, stationery, signage and livery.

The client is a successful vet in London who had already commissioned two other identities for his practice and an accident and emergency service for animals. The brief was to give his pet shop a strong and fun branding that would stand out in the high street.

The project was commissioned in September 2000 and the shop opened in November of the same year.

1 Shop Front Signage
2 Shop Side Wall
3 Branded Delivery Van
4 Stationery

2   3

2. When two established wine merchants owned by Bulmers plc decided to merge they came to HGV to generate a new brand name, design a new identity and rationalise the new wine catalogue. The project included extending the identity to lorry graphics, stationery, promotional materials and sub-branding for direct telephone sales.

1 Wine Catalogue
2 Promotional Wine Glass
3 Mailer announcing the merger of two wine companies
4 Promotional Gift

for the modern
metropolitan pet
veterinary owned

351 archway road
highgate
london N6 5AA

T 020 8341 4888
F 020 8340 8211
E mail@highgatepet.com

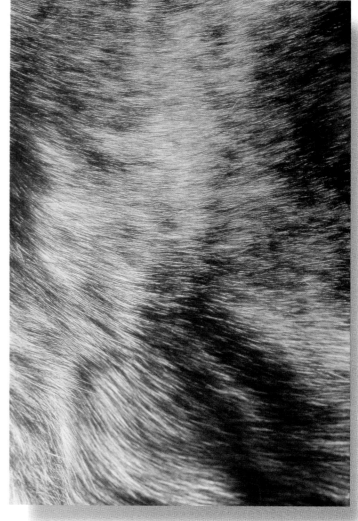

4

for the modern
metropolitan pet
veterinary owned

351 archway road
highgate
london N6 5AA

T 020 8341 4888
F 020 8340 8211
E mail@highgatepet.com

Neil Statham

for the modern
metropolitan pet
veterinary owned

351 archway road
highgate
london N6 5AA

T 020 8341 4888
F 020 8340 8211
E mail@highgatepet.com

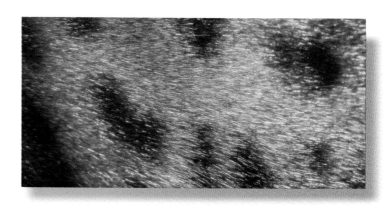

FOLIO

a new world of wine

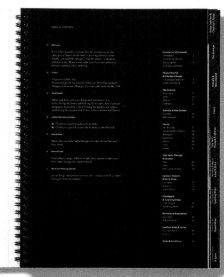

1

3

4

The Identica Partnership

Management: Michael Peters, Tom Austin,
Carole Laugier, Ruth Goddard, Karen O'Neill
Contacts: Damian Schogger, Brenda Lardner
Staff: 70
Founded: 1992

Newcombe House:
45 Notting Hill Gate
London W11 3LQ
t: +44 (0)20 7569 5600/f: +44 (0)20 7569 5656
email: info@identica.com
www.identica.com

The Identica Partnership is an award-winning total communications company. Through our two consultancies, Identica and Tango, the company embraces strategic brand consultancy and management, corporate identity, packaging, literature design, youth marketing, brand expression, retail and environment design, advertising, naming, digital media, new product development and point-of-sale design.

Over sixty per cent of our business is international and we have access to an extensive worldwide network. Through our London offices, we work in partnership with our clients to help them improve their company performance by building powerful, distinctive, compelling and timeless brands.

1

1. Leumi - A radical rebranding of Bank Leumi, Israel's second largest bank, including the creation of a new corporate identity, signage, stationery, credit cards, and a range of corporate and banking literature.
2. Reebok Strikezone - Brand identity and in-store communications for Strikezone - Reebok's new range of football boots - which linked the art of playing football directly to magic.
3. emax - A new brand identity and visual language for leading Russian online portal emax, along with the retail environment and branding for its new Internet cafés - cafémax.
4. Passaggio - New name, corporate identity, literature, signage, environments and packaging for Swiss catering company Schweizerische Speisewagen-Gesellschaft (SSG).
5. Russian Standard - The creation and positioning of a super-premium vodka brand called Russian Standard for Russian drinks distribution company, Roust Inc.
6. Chivas Regal 12 - Revitalisation of labelling and new communications programme for Chivas Regal, the world's leading premium Scotch whisky.

home   mail   sport   chat   my   clubs   shopping   bar

THE HAT-TRICK

2

3

5

6

 search
 news
 business
 travel
 jobs
 photo

25 Store Street
South Crescent
London WC1E 7BL
t: +44 (0)20 7323 3300
email: questions@imagination.com
www.imagination.com

Imagination

"The range of Imagination's work stretches conventional definitions of design" Stephen Bayley

"Imagination is an ideas company. If there's a hierarchy, it's creativity before execution. That's one of the reasons I enjoy going there - because I feel stimulated creatively."
J Mays, Vice President, Design, Ford Motor Company

Imagination has worked with the world's leading brands for over 25 years to become a global agency with offices in London, New York, Detroit, Hong Kong, Tokyo and Stockholm. It has a culture as distinctive as its name. The quality of its people, the integrity of its thought and its uncompromising commitment to creativity, ultimately defines its approach.

Imagination pioneered the idea of brand experience. That is, not just what a brand communicates in two dimensions, but the emotions, feelings and responses it can arouse in all dimensions. It has achieved this through its unique multi-disciplinary offer, employing architects, interior designers, graphic designers, writers, film makers, photographers, lighting and multimedia experts, all under one roof.

In such a truly multi-disciplinary environment, it's no wonder that Imagination's graphic design team creates work that stretches from print, through brand expression, to environmental graphics and installations. Imagination gives designers the opportunity to expand their input beyond the traditional boundaries of graphic design. And to consider visual communication as an integral and enhancing part of any experience.

See also section New Media Design p. 116
See also volume Interior, Retail and Event Design p. 38

1-2. Environment and booklet proposal, Mazda. Design: Andrew Monk
3-5. Fibre optic light installation. Design: Caroline Wilson
6-9. Book design, Journey, The Ford Motor Company. Design: Paul Blackburn
10. Book design, Imagination. Design: Giovanna Lisignoli
11. Invitation, Guinness Storehouse. Design: Peter Goodrick-Clarke
12-15. Book design, Talk, BT. Design: Marcus Maurer
16. Brochures, Ericsson. Design: Brian Griver
17. Invitation, Aston Martin V12 Vanquish preview. Design: Martin Brown

1

2

3

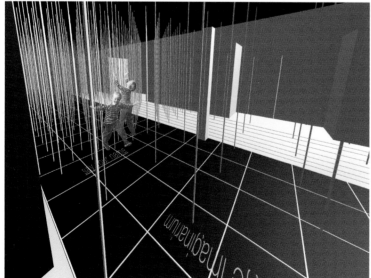

4

5

6

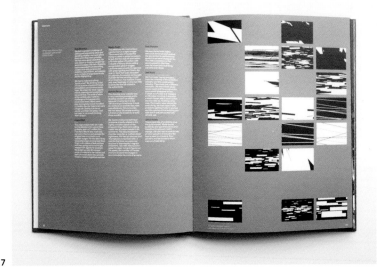

7

8

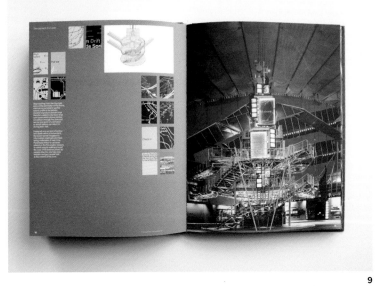

9

10

11

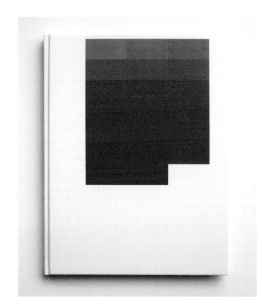

12

13

14

15

16

17

Management: *Kevin Gill*
Contacts: *Lindsey Blythe*
Staff: *12*
Founded: *1993*
Memberships: *Design Business Association*

42 JudgeGill Design Consultancy

3 Cobourg Street
Manchester M1 3GY
t: +44 (0) 161 228 3066/f: +44 (0) 161 228 0137
email: info@judgegill.co.uk
www.judgegill.co.uk

JudgeGill are a design consultancy providing fresh,
progressive design, creating unique solutions for the
retail, leisure and commercial sectors.
Our competencies include spatial design, graphics
branding and project implementation

From your initial idea, our process explores project
context, matching team skills to key design stages.
In our relationships with clients, consultants and
manufacturers, collaboration is essential.

Sharing knowledge and ideas encourages participation
and enjoyment, whilst maintaining a sense of humour.
We believe creativity isn't measured by budget.

Clients
JD Sports Plc
French Connection
Adidas
Ted Baker
New Look
size?
Virgin
Homes4u

See also volume Interior, Retail and Event Design p. 42

Project ref.
345-AB-0202
Image 01

01. JudgeGill promotional T-shirt.
02. JudgeGill brochure 2001.
03. Cobra graphics & branding.
04. Cobra promtional poster.
05. Kickers concept bag.
06. One Central Street graphics.

Project ref.
452-AB-0302
Image 02

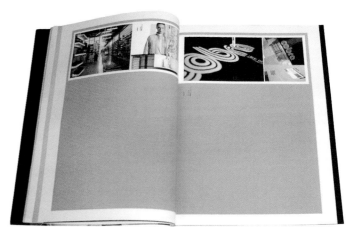

Project ref.
342-FP-0800
Image 03

Project ref.
342-AB-1000
Image 04

Project ref.
485-AB-0401
Image 05

Project ref.
362-AB-0402
Image 06

Lewis Moberly
Brand Identity

Management: Mary Lewis, Robert Moberly
Contacts: Robert Moberly, Dr. Hilary Boys
Staff: 28
Founded: 1984
Memberships: British Design & Art Direction,
Design Business Association

London Office:
33 Gresse street
London W1T 1QU
t: +44 (0) 20 7580 9252/f: +44 (0) 20 7255 1671
email: robert.moberly@lewismoberly.com
www.lewismoberly.com

Paris Office:
112 AV Kleber
75116 Paris
France
t: +33 14 755 7434/f: +33 14 755 7437
email: patrice.civanyan@lewismoberly.com

profile

We are an international brand identity consultancy based in London and Paris with affiliates in New York. Formed in 1984 by designer Mary Lewis and strategic director Robert Moberly, the company's expertise is in brand strategy and design. This includes Visual Intelligence™ (our strategic planning process), brand and corporate identity, packaging design, interactive design, name generation and research. Our diverse portfolio includes projects for brand leaders, retailers, museums, multinationals and privately owned companies. Our reputation is based on vigorous relevance and a passion for excellence. Numerous awards include the British Design & Art Direction Gold Award for Outstanding Design and the Design Business Association Grand Prix Award for Design Effectiveness. In 2001 Mary Lewis was presented with the British Design & Art Direction President's Award.

clients

Alfred Dunhill
Allied Domecq
Champagne Bollinger
Christian Dior
Harrods
Jaeger
Jasper Conran
Johnson & Johnson
Kao
Kambly
Le Bon Marché
Marks & Spencer
Novartis
Pernod Ricard
Pol Roger
Procter and Gamble
Remy Martin
Sogrape Vinhos de Portugal S.A.
The Duchy of Cornwall
The Royal Mail
Waitrose Limited
Waterford Wedgwood

See also volume Product and Packaging Design p. 42

1. Stuart Crystal. Brand Identity and packaging design for UK crystal glass manufacturer.
2. La Grande Epicerie de Paris. Corporate identity for the leading Parisian food hall. Client: Le Bon Marché.
3. National Maritime Museum Cornwall. Corporate identity for maritime museum opening in Falmouth, Cornwall in Autumn 2002.

LA GRAN**DE** EPICERIE **PARIS**

NATIONAL MARITIME
MUSEUM CORNWALL

Made Thought

Management: Ben Parker and Paul Austin
Contacts: Ben Parker and Paul Austin
Staff: 3
Founded: 2000

Second Floor:
181 Cannon Street Road
London E1 2LX
t: +44 (0)20 7488 4005
email: info@madethought.com
www.madethought.com

Company Profile
Established in London, 2000.

Clients
Booth-Clibborn Editions
Barbican Art Gallery
MangaJo
MTV
Sculpture at Goodwood
Sonneti
Stella McCartney
Tate Publishing
The Mill

Marsteller

Contacts: Mark Rollinson, William Driscoll, Simon Dryland

24-28 Bloomsbury way
London WC1A 2PX
t: +44 (0)20 7300 6301/f: +44 (0)20 7831 6638
email: mark_rollinson@uk.bm.com

Who is Marsteller?
Marsteller is the brand communication arm of Burson Marsteller. We offer the nimbleness and creativity of a small agency, with the backing of the worldwide resources of WPP Group. Our team comprises an eclectic mix of art directors, copywriters, designers, account directors and PR professionals. We have won many awards for our work both for its creativity and effectiveness.

Our approach
Our objective is to create great ideas that enable our clients to engage their audiences and influence perceptions. We employ an integrated approach to communications. We focus on the desired result and not on the medium. All our solutions are supported by a campaign idea: a long-term intellectual property that brings brand strategy to life creatively and memorably. It is developed before any creative work and can be used in all forms of brand communication.

advertising

Association of Tennis Professionals
advertising revitalising Men's Tennis

Tennis Masters Series
building an elite tournament series

literature

Kingfisher
corporate social responsibility brochure

identity

G-14
THE VOICE OF THE CLUBS

G-14
launching an association of Europe's biggest football clubs

branding

Shell Renewables
demonstrating Shell's commitment to renewable energy

integrated

WestQuay Shopping Centre
surrounding shoppers with a launch message

Neujuice Design

Management: Nick Davis and Emma Papper
Contacts: Nick Davis
Staff: 3
Founded: 1998

Gloucester House
45 Gloucester Street
Brighton BN1 4EW
t: +44(0)1273 688872/f: +44(0)1273 602440
email: info@neujuice.com
www.neujuice.com

profile

For the past four years Neujuice Design have produced
successful interactive and traditional media projects
focusing on enhancing our clients' brand values. We
have worked with a range of clients from independent
producers through to international organisations such
as FTSE and the BBC.

Neujuice's expertise includes brand identity, print,
web design and e-business development. Our aim is
to combine visual creativity and technical ingenuity to
provide marketing solutions that bring real business
benefits to our clients.

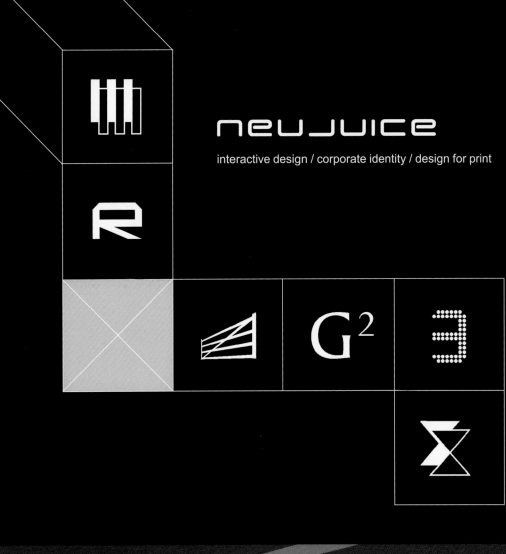

interactive design / corporate identity / design for print

Redhead Design

Management: Laura Danby and James Keeffe
Contacts: Laura Danby
Staff: 3
Founded: 1998

Gloucester House
45 Gloucester Street
Brighton BN1 4EW
t: +44(0) 1273 602440/f: +44(0)1273 602440
email: info@redheaddesign.com
www.redheaddesign.com

profile

Redhead design, established in 1998, is a friendly
Brighton-based partnership with a reputation for
innovative work in design and print. We are a group of
professionals with core skills in packaging, advertising,
corporate design, magazine design, online branding,
e-business and internet solutions.

Clients include ASDA, Ascari, Boots, Compaq, E2E
Solutions, Euroboss, First Choice, GNC Livewell,
Harrods, Honeywill & Stein, International Diabetes
Federation, National Street Arts Festival, Norwich
Union, Six Continents Hotels, Tesco's, Twinlab and
many more!

Redhead are always ready to find individual creative
solutions for each client. Please contact us to see how
we can help your business.

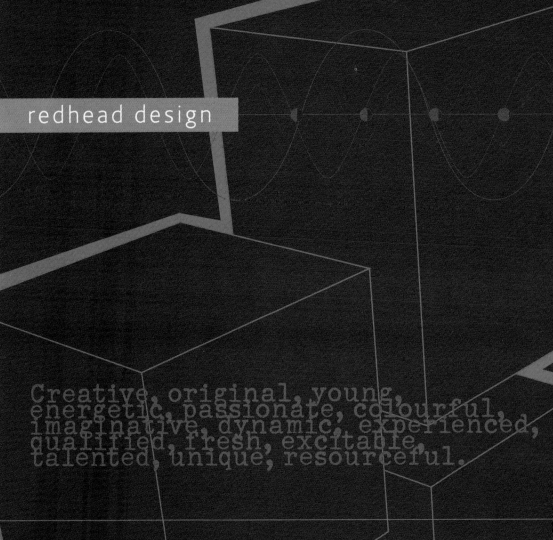

www.neujuice.com

RURAL FUTURES

01.   02.   03.

01. Pembroke Financial Services
02. SND
03. Ocuguard
04. Advantage Magazine
05. ASDA Vitamins
06. Ascari Website

04.   05.   06.

Oakwood dc
Stategic integrated design

Management: Phil Marshall / Neil Sims / Chris Jones
Contacts: Phil Marshall / Chris Jones
Staff: 42
Founded: 1995
Memberships: British Design Initiative / Institute of Directors

7 Park Street
Bristol BS1 5NF
t: +44 (0)11 7983 6789/f: +44 (0)11 7983 7323
email: user@oakwood-dc.com
www.oakwood-dc.com

Company profile

Oakwood dc was founded by three partners who shared the vision of ensuring their clients' commercial success by consistently delivering creative and impactful design, combined with a high quality cost service. From this beginning in 1995, Oakwood dc has grown into a strategic design consultancy that spans three inter-related disciplines:

Oakwood sd specialises in strategic graphic design from corporate identity, branding and literature through to packaging and direct mail. Oakwood 3d concentrates on designing and building the structures that make up creative retail and leisure environments, while Oakwood idc works exclusively with screen-based media to create dynamic websites, database-driven applications, CD-Rom presentations and interactive animations.

The strength of Oakwood dc is its team of individual characters and personalities, with diverse backgrounds and experiences. Our talented team works hand-in-hand with company professionals from various industries to ensure that the commercial relationship between the product or brand and the creative design is guaranteed.

See also section New Media Design p. 118
See also volume Interior, Retail and Event Design p. 46

1. Product identity and launch material for Castrol GTX Magnatect performance oil. Castrol North Western 2002.

NEW
Precision Pouring

Castrol

GTX
Magnatec

Protection From The Moment You Turn The Key

Synthetic Engineering

P811679

4.5L e

The Open Agency
Creative Intelligence

Management: Mike Horseman (Managing Director), Gary Cooke (Creative Director)
Contacts: Mike Horseman and Victoria Batty
Staff: 22
Founded: 1983
Memberships: D&AD, DBA, RSA

Mill House:
8 Mill Street
London SE1 2BA
t: +44 (0)20 7740 7000/f: +44 (0)20 7740 7001
email: mike.horseman@openagency.com
www.openagency.com

The Open Agency is a design company specialising in Brand Identity & Literature, Packaging, and New Media. Our ability to comprehend what needs to be communicated is coupled with our inventiveness - ultimately resulting in a strong and original concept.

We believe that informality and openness isn't contradictory to good business, and ensures our full understanding of our customers' requirements. By being open and honest, with both our clients and ourselves, we have developed a working environment that is fun, yet commercial. Only by being truly open and approachable do we best represent our clients' interests.

See also section New Media Design p. 120

1

1. Summer tree festive mailer
2. Timberland training literature
3. Royal Mail promotional poster
4-5. Posters developed for the International Committee for the Red Cross

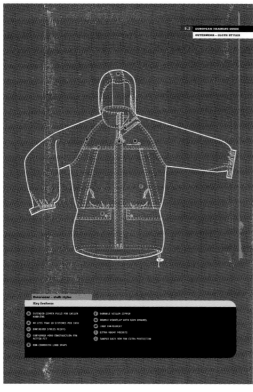

2

3

4

5

56

OPX
Visual
Communication

Management: William Bickerstaff, Simon Goodall,
Antony Harrington, Frances Jackson
Contacts: Simon Goodall, Frances Jackson
Staff: 6
Founded: 1992
Memberships: D&AD, DBA, STD

51 Hoxton Square
London N1 6PB
t: +44 (0)20 7428 0683/f: +44 (0)20 7428 0684
email: post@opx.co.uk
www.opx.co.uk

Company profile
OPX strive to create work that is intelligent, beautiful
and effective. Our work is characterised by an honesty
of approach and flexibility in thinking, and a determination to offer the highest standard of strategic
direction, creative thinking, design, production and
project management. We solve problems in print,
3D and digital media using a strong understanding
of the related industries, their processes and techniques, to make clear and informed decisions on the
most effective routes of production whether in print,
CD, Internet or signage.

Recent clients
Abbey National
Bible Society
BRE
Cityspace
FaberMaunsell
Interface
Vision On

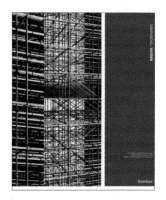

1. Project: Dimensions. Product brochure for new range of
printed flooring. Client: Interface
2. Campaign: Pure Modularity. Pan-European brand awareness campaign incorporating poster, website, and CD ROM.
Client: Interface
3. Project: Corporate identity and visual language for all print
and digital communications. Client: FaberMaunsell

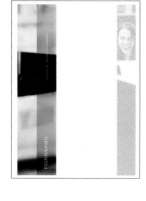

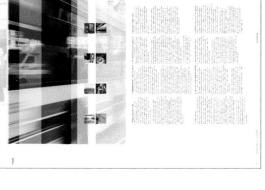

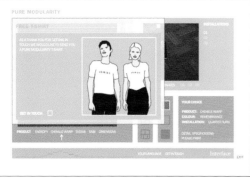

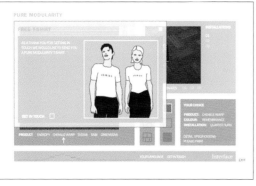

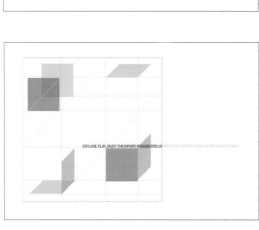

…in FaberMaunsell, we have the people, the skills, the resources, the opportunities and the will to create a modern consultancy that is capable of making a major difference to the way people live, work and travel, now and in the future.

FABER MAUNSELL

Plum Partnership
Corporate Design

Management: *Sue Wells*
Contacts: *Sue Wells*
Staff: *6*
Founded: *1996*

83 Charlotte Street
London W1T 4PR
t: +44 (0)20 7637 7767/f: +44(0)20 7637 3111
email: info@plum-partnership.demon.co.uk
www.plumpartnership.com

Company Profile
Fresh ideas. Smart thinking. Direct Approach.

Plum Partnership is a multi-discipline design agency
spanning many sectors, including corporate design,
fashion, automotive, retail, financial, marketing,
magazine publishing, exhibition and display graphics.
Primarily targeting design for print, Plum also fulfils
clients' requirements in areas of website and
multimedia design.

The agency was established in 1997 by three partners
with diverse but complementary skills. We believe that
what makes Plum different is our fresh, smart and
direct approach, and our desire for people to enjoy the
experience of doing buiness with us.

Clients
AMP Asset Management
Bravissimo
Bridgestore Firestone
British Airways
Burberry
Carswell Gould
Centurion Group
Christopher Wray
CNN International
Deutsche Bank
The International Red Cross
Isis
The London Stock Exchange
Princes Trust
Proshare
Rosenblatt Solicitors
Selfridges
Tesco
Tencel
Toyota
Virgin
The Windsmoor Group

1. Toyota: Pan-European brochure
2. Burberry: Golf Catalogue
3. The Windsmoor Group: Precis Collection brochure
4. Deutsche Bank: Pensions Administrators brochure
5. Selfridges: Account Customer magazines

1 Toyota | AUTOMOTIVE

2 Burberry | FASHION

3 The Windsmoor Group | FASHION

4 Deutsche Bank | FINANCIAL

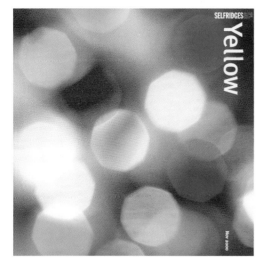

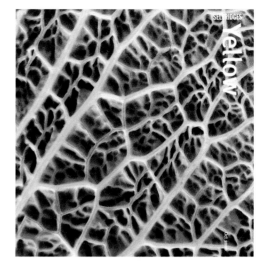

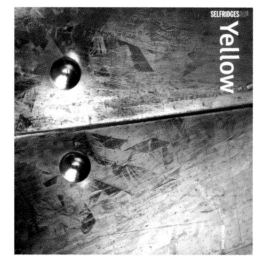

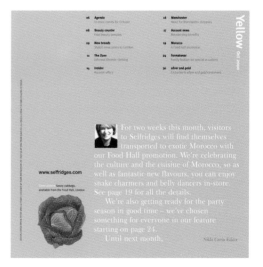

Rebecca Fairman Design
Graphic Design & Communications

Management: Rebecca Fairman
Contacts: Rebecca Fairman
Staff: 4
Founded: 1991

5 Calvert Avenue
London E2 7JP
t: +44 (0)20 7613 4300/f: +44 (0)20 7613 4400
email: rebecca@rebeccafairmandesign.co.uk

60

With over 19 years experience in advertising and design, Rebecca Fairman established her own company in 1991 offering design communications with a mix of creativity, service and strategic thinking for individuals and small businesses, through to international retailers.
We know that service and attention to detail are as important as design skills. Clients work directly with designers, which eliminates confusion and establishes a better working relationship.
Our pricing structure is fair and competitive, and we will do our utmost to offer you value for money.

Client List
Banana Split Planners & Productions
Double G Communications
Flag Telecom
Kookaï
KP:C Communications
Lillywhites
London Research and development
Mappin & Webb Jewellers
Mattel Games
Miss Selfridge
Telme.com
The Body Shop
Warners

1

5

6

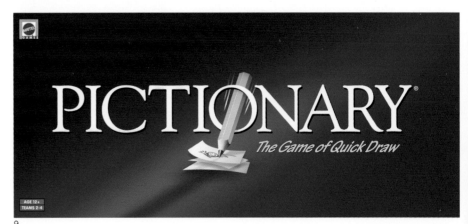

9

1. Exterior signage for Knightsbridge 8m hoarding, Kookaï 2002
2. Seasonal carrier bag, Kookaï 2002
3. Seasonal carrier bag, Kookaï 2001
4. POS promotional material, Miss Selfridge 2002
5. Jewellery brochure & display materials, Mappin & Webb 2001
6. Silverwear brochure & display materials, Mappin & Webb 2002
7. Visual merchandising window & instore POS, Lillywhites 2001
8. Product catalogue, The Body Shop 2001
9. Games packaging for Pictionary, Mattel 2002
10. Games packaging for Outburst, Mattel 2001
11. Games packaging ThinkBlot, Mattel 2000
12. Customer Club Identity and literature, The Body Shop 2002
13. Corporate identity and literature, Flag Telecom 2001

2

3

4

7

8

10

11

12

13

Redpath
words & pictures

Management: Richard Irvine, Iain Lauder,
Andrew Hunter
Contacts: Allison Traynor
Staff: 21
Founded: 1995
Memberships: DBA, D&AD, Marketing Society,
BDI, EDI

5 Gayfield Square
Edinburgh EH1 3NW
t: +44 (0)131 556 9115/f: +44 (0)131 556 9116
email: wordsandpictures@redpath.co.uk
www.redpath.co.uk

The future is words and pictures

One day we may not be so different, but for the
moment we are. Very few graphic design consultancies
employ writers, as we do. And as far as we know,
we're the only one to have writers working alongside
designers on every project from start to finish. That's
because we believe in the power of words and pictures.
Both count, in every business message, so we make
sure we treat them as equals.

Client list

The Royal Bank of Scotland Group
Highland Distillers Brands
Grampian Country Food Group
Orkney Tourist Board
The Scottish Executive
Ethicon
NCR (Scotland)
University of Edinburgh Management School
British Council Scotland
The Royal Society for Arts

See also volume Product and Packaging Design p. 48

British Council Scotland

Moving with the times

1

1. Moving with the times, British Council Scotland
2. NHS Scotland Corporate Identity, The Scottish Executive
3. Corporate Stationery, Bang On Displays
4. Explore Orkney 2001, Orkney Tourist Board
5. Easy Peasy Sweetie Pie, Ebury Press

3

4

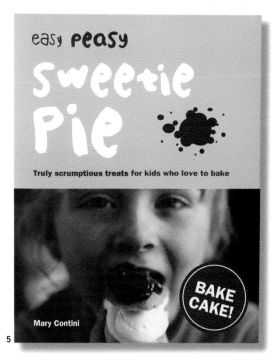

5

River Design Ltd
River Design

Management: Antony Lawrence, Peter Widdup
Contacts: Antony or Peter
Staff: 12
Founded: 1994

River Studios
84 Bendemeer Road
Putney
London SW15 1JU
t: +44 (0)20 8780 2081/f: +44 (0)20 8780 2082
email: info@riverdesign.com
www.riverdesign.com

River Design is a team of highly talented and
experienced designers offering a broad range of skills.
We pride ourselves on our 'can do' attitude and flexible
service approach.

The team you choose to work with must understand
your business, your brand, your offer, the position you
are in and where you want to be - they must have a
breadth of experience and be capable of creating new
and fresh ideas that are distinctive and appropriate.

The process should be challenging but at the same
time enjoyable, with the project growing from joint
thinking between client and designer.

Finally, you want to be sure that the project will be
managed effectively - on time, on budget.

River Design ... just add water

Recent clients include
Alliance & Leicester
Apple Computers
Arcadian Hotels
Banco International de Mozambique
Barclays Bank plc
BHS
Blue Circle plc
British Airways Holidays
Browns Hotel
Carlton Tower
Finnamore Management
Gillette/Duracell
Heritage Hotels
Hyatt International
Jones Lang Lasalle
Montes Club (Jamie Oliver)
One Aldwych
Portobello Hotel
Pretty Polly
Sara Lee Courtaulds
Save the Children
Siemens Medical
Staal Bankiers
The Edge Video Co
The Whitehouse
Thomson Holidays
Whitmuir Management Consultants
Whitney Tyzack
WWF International

refr

Exhibition

A series of 12 posters for Hyatt
Hotels at the NEC Birmingham,
also used in advertising and linked
to website via a range of dynamic
prefixes to the URL.

Direct Mail

4 seasonal mailers for Heritage
Hotels. The most successful
autumn mailer netted a
9 to 1 return on investment
and won the Hotel Marketing
Award in 2001.

Promotions/Website

Creating an exciting range of
colourful flyers to match the
redesign of the entire website.
The hit rate increased from 5,000
to 50,000 with most viewers
penetrating at least 6 pages.

eshing

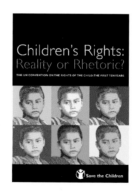

Clothing Packaging

Redesigned and launched all of Pretty Polly hosiery and underwear packaging within the drapery sector over the last 3 years with a special emphasis on image and naming products.

Food Packaging

Design of packaging for a new ice cream and sorbet range launched in the UK in 2002. The top 4 supermarkets bought in at concept packaging stage. The product range is soon to be greatly extended.

Print

Literature for charities including Save the Children and The World Wide Fund For Nature. Producing publications, guidelines and research documents to help promote good causes.

Corporate

Creating logos and identities for a number of clients including a range of credit cards for the Alliance & Leicester. We have also produced guidelines and templates for two large banks in Holland and Mozambique.

New Media

Product launch for Duracell including electronic sales media and literature for the total sales force. Elements of the design were then fast-tracked to the USA to be used on packaging.

Rufus Leonard

Management: *Neil Svensen, Principal Director;*
Steve Howell, Executive Creative Director;
Andrew Pinkess, Strategy Director
Contacts: *Zoe Shortis*
Staff: *100*
Founded: *1989*
Memberships: *British Interactive Media Association*

The Drill Hall
57a Farringdon Road
London EC1M 3JB
t: +44 (0)20 7404 4490/f: +44 (0)20 7404 4491
email: newbusiness@rufusleonard.com
www.rufusleonard.com

Since its foundation in 1989, Rufus Leonard has
become one of the UK's leading brand and digital
business consultancies.

We combine great marketing ideas and technology
in the space where organisations must be more
effective than ever: in the ways they communicate
with customers, or stakeholders, and in the flow of
information between these groups.

Digital media works interactively in this flow, and in
this flow brand comes alive.

Ideas \ Brand \ Technology

See also section New Media Design p. 124

TOWER HAMLETS

nucoda

M&G

propeller

Rufus Leonard

Ideas Technology Brand

Saatchi & Saatchi Design

Management: Simon Steel - Managing Director,
Debbie Orrell - Client Services Director, Iain Ross -
Design Director, Ian Lanksbury - Design Director
Contacts: Simon Steel, Debbie Orrell
Staff: 25

89 Whitfield Street
London W1T 4HG
t: +44 (0)20 7307 5327/f: +44 (0)20 7307 5328
email: ssteel@saatchi-design.com
www.saatchi-design.com

Company profile

Saatchi & Saatchi Design is part of TfG, the biggest on-site production unit in Europe. We provide creative solutions and integrated resources for brand positioning, naming, corporate and brand identity, interactive media and broadcast design.

Clients

Aspective - Corporate identity/literature
BBC - Programme identity
Bulmers - Annual report & accounts
Camelot - Corporate identity/literature
CCSD/Fuel - Corporate identity
Comic Relief - Fundraising literature
Crone Corkill - Literature & website
Energy Savings Trust/Future Energy - identity/literature
Hampstead Theatre - Branding/literature
Hewlett Packard - Branding
3i - Literature
KPMG - Branding
LIFFE - Product marketing, branding and annual report & accounts
Linklaters & Alliance - Corporate identity/literature
Metropolitan Police - Divisional identity
National Lottery - Corporate identity/branding/POS/literature
Premier Oil - Annual report & accounts/literature/website
PPG Autocolor - Global press advertising
Schroders - Annual report & accounts
Toyota Europe - Brand Identity/Pan-European literature system
Visa - Brand positioning for Europe & CEMEA regions

See also section New Media Design p. 126

1. LIFFE (London International Financial Futures Exchange) - Swapnote product identity, positioning and through-the-line campaign
2. Toyota - Pan European corporate literature system
3. BBC - Newsround identity and title sequence
4. BBC - The Saturday Show identity and title sequence
5. Crone Corkill - Puzzle from the corporate brochure, part of the integrated puzzle campaign

1

DISCOVER

2

CREATE

3

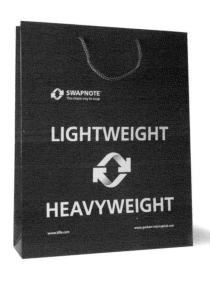

PERCEIVE

CHALLENGE

ENJOY

SMILE

5

How much can you soak up?
Problem: A wet sponge weighs 1kg and is 99% water by weight. Squeeze it so that it is only 98% water by weight. How much does it weigh now?

Solved: 500g

For more solutions visit
www.cronecorkill.co.uk

SAATCHI & SAATCHI
DESIGN

Sears Davies
Corporate identity, corporate literature and digital design

Management: Julian Davies, Stewart Webber, Ben Tobin, Craig Stafford
Contacts: Julian Davies
Staff: 16
Founded: 1988
Memberships: CSD

25A Copperfield Street
London SE1 0EN
t: +44 (0)20 7633 0939/f: +44 (0)20 7633 9953
email: info@searsdavies.com
www.searsdavies.com

A unique combination of design talent and strategic thinking has enabled Sears Davies to establish an enviable position within the corporate communications sector. Through listening to our clients' objectives and sharing ideas, we help them to achieve commercial success by delivering inspirational and effective design solutions.

Active in all areas of graphic design, we continue to demonstrate our skills in the creation of corporate identity and branding, company literature and annual reports, digital design, promotional campaigns and direct mail initiatives for an enviable portfolio of clients.

Clients
Allsport
Associated Capital Theatres
British Gas
Charnos plc
CIS Insurance
Crown Office Chambers
Dar Al-Handasah (Shair and Partners)
Department of Trade & Industry
Eastern Electricity plc
Export Credits Guarantee Department
Foreign & Commonwealth Office
Generali SpA
Greenland Interactive
Heath Lambert Group
Highways Agency
Imperial College
Leo Burnett
Lloyds TSB Group Union
London Electricity plc
London Transport Buses
Macfarlanes
Macmillan Cancer Relief Fund
Matrix Securities
Memery Crystal
Merrill Lynch Investment Managers
Museum of Garden History
Natural History Museum
One Essex Court
Pantaenius
Property Bar Association
Simon Petroleum Technology
Speciality Retail Group
Welsh Rugby Union

See also section New Media Design p. 128

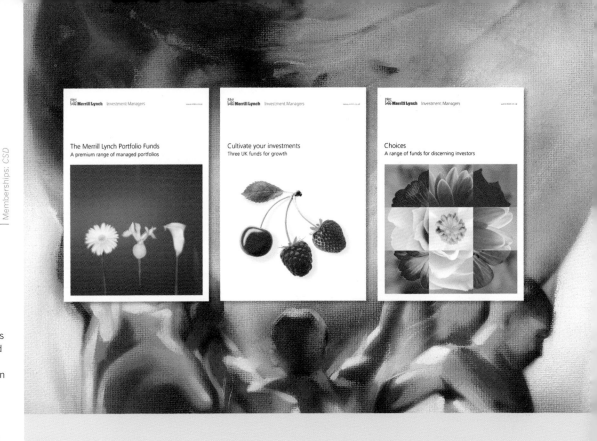

The Merrill Lynch Portfolio Funds
A premium range of managed portfolios

Cultivate your investments
Three UK funds for growth

Choices
A range of funds for discerning investors

We have yet to find another design group that provides such a high level of creative thought and originality as Sears Davies. This, coupled with their thorough understanding of the requirements of our industry, makes them very special.

Rick Andrews, Director, Head of EMEA Retail Marketing
Merrill Lynch Investment Managers

www.heathlambert.com

Heath Lambert Group
on target
the future of risk management

www.dargroup.com

THE SECRET TO THE *Perfect* GIN & TONIC

identities & brands | literature | promotional campaigns | retail graphics | digital design

searsdaviesdesigners

www.macfarlanes.co.uk

Sharpedge Design and Communication

Management: Diana Inglis and Lloyd Clater
Contacts: Diana Inglis / Lloyd Clater
Founded: 1992

1 Silex Street
LONDON SE1 0DP
t: +44 (0)20 7633 0003/f: +44 (0)20 7633 0020
email: contact@sharpedge.co.uk
www.sharpedge.co.uk

10 years of effective solutions

Sharpedge Design and Communication
was established in 1992 and celebrated ten successful
years in April 2002.

The consultancy works closely with clients to develop
ideas that meet the aims and objectives of any project.
Our work is identifiable by its combination of function
and craftsmanship, combined with a deep understanding of design and marketing and the role they
play in successful business ventures.

Our field is graphic design and new media and
Sharpedge has been involved with several major
advertising campaigns, land regeneration projects,
corporate identities, promotional material, on-line
communications, video production and various 3D
installations for many large organisations.

Sharpedge is committed to working closely with
clients to provide award-winning design and effective
marketing strategies, that are on time and within
budget.

See also section New Media Design p. 130

Calor Gas Village of the Year 2002
ENGLAND & WALES

entry forms
& guidelines

NEW IDEAS, NEW APPROACHES, NEW OPPORTUNITIES   A STRATEGY FRAMEWORK FOR THE DEVELOPMENT OF THE ARTS IN SOUTHWARK

MARYLEBONE VILLAGE

entry form & guidelines
entry form & guidelines

natural cooling

Village
ne Village

rural dimension

CALOR'S COMMITMENT TO THE COUNTRYSIDE

the greener dimension

Annual Student Awards
INVITATION

ten years of effective solutions

Start Design Ltd
Brand identity, Interactive media, Marketing communication

Management: Mike Curtis and Darren Whittingham
Contacts: Mike Curtis and Darren Whittingham
Staff: 55
Founded: 1996
Memberships: DMA, Trust UK, CIM, DP Data Protection, Design Business Association, SPCA, British Design Initiative

Kingsbourne House
229-231 High Holborn
London WC1V 7DA
t: +44 (0)20 7269 0101/f: +44 (0)20 7269 0102
email: mike@startdesign.com
www.startdesign.com

Profile
Start Design gets results. Specialising in brand identity, interactive media and marketing communications, the agency develops award-winning solutions by placing the emphasis on strategy and ideas. Its creativity is driven by the needs of customers and the objectives of clients. Working with major UK and international organisations, Start has the design, copywriting and project management expertise to deliver complete solutions across all media.

Clients
Avis
COI Communications
Consignia
Eurobell/Telewest
Flextech Television
Home Office
Land Registry
Ordance Survey
Parcel Force
Post Office
Royal Mail
thetrainline
The Times
Virgin Atlantic
Virgin Books
Virgin.com
Virgin Holidays
Virgin Management Ltd
Virgin Mobile
Virgin Money
Virgin One Account
Virgin V.Shop
Virgin Wines
Xchanging
Wolseley

See also section New Media Design p. 132

1. A selection of corporate identities, 1996-2002
2. Re-branding and livery design, Virgin Atlantic, 1999
3. Upper Class product brochure, Virgin Atlantic, 2000
4. Retail environment, Virgin V.Shop, 2001
5. 3-D winter catalogue, Virgin Mobile, 2001
6. Corporate brochure, Royal Mail International Services, 2001
7. Young Letter-Writers competition, Royal Mail, 2000

1

6

INTERNATIONAL MAIL
SEND IT WORLD CLASS

Introducing our International Mailing Services
from 4 June 2001

Royal Mail

Sending invoices, statements and
general correspondence worldwide

7

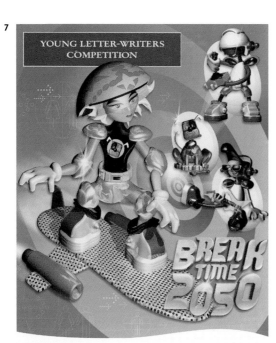

YOUNG LETTER-WRITERS
COMPETITION

BREAK
TIME
2050

Imagine YOU could travel
50 years into the future.
What hobbies and games
will kids be playing? What are the
games we play now be like then?

Royal Mail

Cyber Pup

Streeten Design

Contacts: Roger Streeten
Staff: 5
Founded: 1994

studio2:
42 Kingsway Place
Sans Walk
London EC1R 0LU
t: +44(0) 20 7336 7033/f: +44 (0) 20 7336 7099
email: info@streeten.com
www.streeten.com

Streeten Design, established in 1994 by creative
director Roger Streeten, is a multifaceted design
company located in the heart of London's Clerkenwell.
The company has created websites and print work for
major retailers, international charities and prestigious
bespoke businesses.

Client List
Braitrim plc
Camden Partnership
Capital Sales
Hazel Barton
Joseph Koniak
Jaques Samuel
Mothercare
Osborne Clarke OWA
Royal Free Hospital
Royal Hospital, Chelsea
Saxonbury Executive
Susan Van Meter Interiors
Walkers Quay
Wellcome Trust
Wizcard

1. Packaging & Ticketing for Babyware Range, Mothercare.
2. Programme/Brochure, The Royal Hospital, Chelsea.
3. Educational Pack, The Wellcome Trust.
4. Information Leaflets, The Royal Free Hospital.
5. Web Site, Capital Sales Estate Agent.
6. Web Site, Saxonbury Executive Search & Recruitment.

1

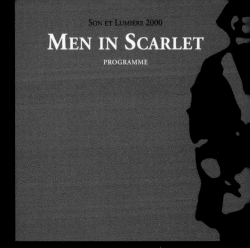

2

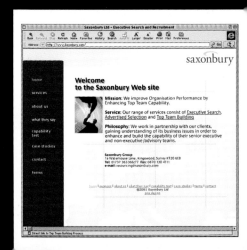

4

Subliminal

Management: Jonathan Taylor-Horne
Contacts: Daisy Zuidyk and Gordon Druce
Staff: 10
Founded: 1997

4 Chapel Row
Queens Square
Bath BA1 1HN
t: +44 (0)1225 401 333/f: +44 (0)1225 402 031
email: info@subliminal.co.uk
www.subliminal.co.uk

Company profile

Subliminal is a multi-disciplinary creative agency whose work is built on solid concepts; creative and conceptual thinking always to the fore. Subliminal continually cast aside convention to deliver new kinds of visual communication, with the teams' experience covering: art direction, 2D/3D design, film and photography, illustration, copywriting and interactive design comprising: websites, CD-ROM/DVD production, animation and sound design.

Stimulate. Communicate. Innovate.

Expertise

Advertising. Brand Identity. Packaging. Point-of-Sale. Marketing. Interactive Design. Moving Image.

Clients include

BBC
Berkeley PR
Channel 4
Chase de Vere
Eidos Interactive
Electronic Arts
EMI
English National Opera
Future Publishing
Mercury Music
Oasis Stores
Ourprice
Polygram
Ricoh UK
Scot-Baker Agency
Shellys
Sony Computer Entertainment
Universal Music
Virgin
Warner Vision

See also section New Media Design p. 134

MAILER 01
LIMITED STOCK
PLEASE ENQUIRE

MAILER 02
AVAILABLE NOW
PLEASE ENQUIRE

1999 CALENDAR
LIMITED STOCK
PLEASE ENQUIRE

▲ IMAGE01. ABOVE. VIEW FROM LEFT TO RIGHT
01 WIPEOUT FUSION / SONY COMPUTER ENTERTAINMENT EUROPE (SCEE) 02 SPEED FREAKS / SCEE
03 COOLBOARDERS 3 / SCEE 04 & 05 KITACHI / REACT MUSIC 06 360 / CRYO 07 'PS2 PRE-ORDER' BOOKLET / SCEE
08 ICO / SCEE 09 ABOMINATION / EIDOS INTERACTIVE 10 WIPEOUT FUSION & AIRBLADE / SCEE
11 'TUNE IN' DL LEAFLET / ENGLISH NATIONAL OPERA

ACCESS TO UPPER FLOOR
LEVEL 03 / SCREEN
SEE 'NEW MEDIA/BROADCAST' PAGE

SUBLIMINAL LOWER FLOOR / LEVEL 02 / PRINT
SUBLIMINAL PRINT COLOUR REFERENCES:
SPOT: PANTONE 8943C / CMYK: 0/60/100/10

▼ IMAGE02. BELOW. VIEW FROM LEFT TO RIGHT. TOP THEN BOTTOM

01 WIPEOUT FUSION / SCEE   02 VAN MORRISON 'DOWN THE ROAD' / POLYDOR RECORDS   03 & 07 ICO / SCEE   04 JAMES 'GETTING AWAY WITH IT...LIVE' / WARNER VISION
05 'PS2 PRE-ORDER' BOOKLET / SCEE   06 INTERNAL 'HUMAN RESOURCES' BROCHURE / CHASE DE VERE   08 'INTERNET SECURITY' ILLUSTRATION / MAC USER UK
09 ABOMINATION / EIDOS INTERACTIVE   10 JAMES 'MILLIONAIRES' / MERCURY/UNIVERSAL RECORDS   11 MODEL PORTFOLIO / SCOT-BAKER AGENCY   12 AIRBLADE / SCEE
13 'SYNTHESIS' QUARTERLY MAGAZINE / RICOH UK   14 'GDS' SHOW INVITE / SHELLYS   15 'TUNE IN' DL LEAFLET / ENGLISH NATIONAL OPERA

Thirteen

84

Management: Nick Hand, John Underwood,
Danny Jenkins
Contacts: Nick Hand
Staff: 10
Founded: 1998
Memberships: DBA. CSD. AIGA

9/10 King Street
Bristol BS1 4EQ
t: +44 (0)117 908 1313/f: +44 (0)117 908 1314
email: nick@thirteen.co.uk
www.thirteen.co.uk

Thirteen is a graphic design company.

We consider diversity to be vital ingredient that enables us to design for a variety of sectors.

Thirteen strives to produce innovative and intelligent design systems across a range of media. Our clients operate in technology, broadcasting, retail and the entertainment industries.

01. Ocean estate agents. Corporate identity.
Vehicle livery.
02. Ocean estate agents. Corporate identity.
Property sale boards.
03. Ocean estate agents. Business cards.
04. Hitec-Lotec. Brand identity.
Logo.
05-07. Hitec-Lotec. Brand identity.
Website.
08-09. Hitec-Lotec. Brand identity.
Fold-out poster and CD.
10. Hitec-Lotec. Brand identity.
Exhibition book.
11. Orange. Pension scheme.
Brand identity.

the Orange pension scheme **unrave**

untangled

05.

06.

07.

08.

09.

10.

FURNITURE

relax

Trickett & Webb

Management: Brian Webb, Lynn Trickett,
Andrew Thomas, Colin Sands, Heidi Lightfoot
Contacts: Heidi Lightfoot
Staff: 10
Founded: 1971
Memberships: D&AD, ISTD, CSD

The Factory:
84 Marchmont Street
London WC1N 1RD
t: +44 (0)20 7388 5832/f: +44 (0)20 7387 4287
email: design@tricketts.co.uk
www.trickettandwebb.co.uk

Trickett & Webb were formed in the early seventies
with one aim - to produce exceptional work for
interesting people. Our success is due to the way we
work in close partnership with each individual client.
Everything about our company is geared to this -
our size, our methods, our passion, our thinking.
Every job is different and deserves its own solution.
We pride ourselves on completing projects in time
and on budget. And if awards matter, we win them.

Our range of work includes corporate identity, financial
and promotional literature, web sites, packaging,
environmental and exhibition design; from the smallest
to the largest of clients.

See also volume Product and Packaging Design p. 52

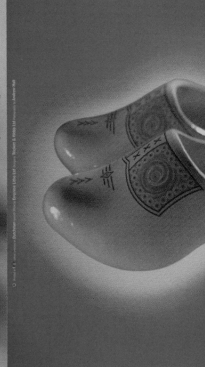

1-4. International Travel Guides for W H Smith; Identity for
the Imperial War Museum Duxford; Corporate design for
Touchstone exhibition and conference organisers; Brand identity
for digital drawing DVD produced by the London Institute
5-8. Gift products for the Royal Society of Arts; Brand launch
for new Dutchman range of papers; Poster for London
Transport exhibition in New York; Brand identity and literature
for Boots Travel and Health Insurance
9-12. London Institute Annual Review and Accounts; Fairbridge
Annual Report; Computer Cab corporate identity; Blackwell
Publishing corporate identity

IOINING THE DOTS TEN ARTISTS +

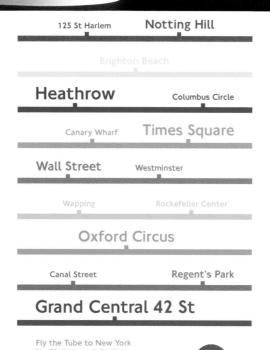

125 St Harlem · Notting Hill

Brighton Beach

Heathrow · Columbus Circle

Canary Wharf · Times Square

Wall Street · Westminster

Wapping · Rockefeller Center

Oxford Circus

Canal Street · Regent's Park

Grand Central 42 St

Fly the Tube to New York
Take off for Heathrow on the Piccadilly line

UNDERGROUND

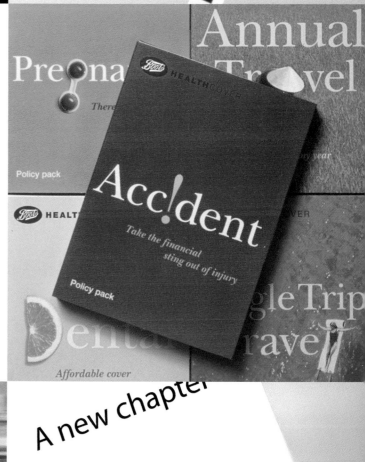

Annual Travel

Pregna

There

Policy pack

Boots HEALTH

Acc!dent

Take the financial
sting out of injury

Policy pack

...gle Trip

Dental ...rave

Affordable cover

10

ComCab

A new chapter

b Blackwell
Publishing

Turner Duckworth
London &
San Francisco

Management: David Turner and Bruce Duckworth
Contacts: Moira Riddell in London, Joanne Chan in San Francisco
Staff: 20
Founded: 1992
Memberships: RSA, DBA

88

Voysey House
Barley Mow Passage
London W4 4PH
t: +44 (0) 20 8994 7190/f: +44 (0) 20 8994 7192
email: moira@turnerduckworth.co.uk
www.turnerduckworth.com

164 Townsend Street, Number 8
94107 San Francisco, California
United States
t: 001 (415) 495 8691/f: 001 (415) 495 8692
email: joanne@turnerduckworth.com
www.turnerduckworth.com

Work Style
Designers on both sides of the Atlantic work on all
projects, so clients benefit from the combination of
British style and American toughness, West Coast
pragmatism combined with London irony.

Philosophy
The company is aptly sized - big enough for the
biggest companies, such as Coca Cola and 3Com but
small enough to allow us to work with newly created
businesses such as The Fresh Olive Company.

Creativity
We have a unique reputation for creating solutions for
clients that are commercially effective and creatively
successful. A well designed brand image stands its
own ground and reinforces its own message. It speaks
for the brand and it speaks for the company that
made it.

Clients
Amazon
BOA UK
Coca Cola UK & Europe
Levis Strauss
Liz Earle Cosmetics
The Fresh Olive Company
Palm
Rank Hovis McDougall
Unilever Bestfoods

See also volume Product and Packaging Design p. 54

1. Brand Identity and packaging for The Fresh Olive Company's
retail range of premium olives oils. Launched November 2000
2. Brand Identity, naming and packaging for Golden State
International's first brand launch - Autumn 2000

Tutssels Enterprise IG

Management: Glenn Tutssel, Beverley Law
Contacts: Richard Sutton
Staff: 20
Founded: 1992
Memberships: D&AD,PAGB,Marketing Society

Greencoat House
Francis Street
England
London SW1P 1DH
t: +44 (0)20 7802 5900/f: +44 (0)20 7802 5801
email: r.sutton@tutssels.com
www.tutssels.com

Tutssels Enterprise IG is a leading brand consultancy specialising in design for what we refer to as 'High Interest' categories, particularly in the drinks and pharmaceuticals sectors.

Our understanding of the dynamics of the premium sector, combined with our award winning creativity and high level of craftsmanship, means we offer a real expertise for brand owners looking for commercially effective branding solutions.

In the last few years, we have created distinctive, iconic and memorable identities that have been commercially effective across all brand platforms. These include visual identity programmes for Smirnoff Ice, The Guinness Rugby World Cup sponsorship , Baileys, Debic Dairy and Panadol.

Our branding offer has now been given greater depth as a result of the merger with Enterprise IG in 2001, the world's largest brand identity consultancy.

See also volume Product and Packaging Design p. 56

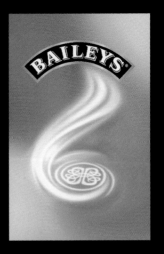

TWO:design
graphic design +
advertising + art
direction + new
media + other
creative stuff.

Management: David Coventon MA, Graham Peake
MA MCSD.
Staff: 4
Founded: 1997

TWO:design/Thinking With Originality
Studio 20. The Arches.
Hartland Road.
London NW1 8HR
t: +44 (0)20 7267 1118/f: +44 (0)20 7482 0221
email: studio@twodesign.co.uk
www.twodesign.co.uk

who are TWO?

GP: David and I started TWO:design in 1997. We had
both worked in design and advertising studios for a
few years and felt that it was time we did our own
thing. We started with work for the music industry, for
The Fugees, however the portfolio has expanded to
include clients in fashion, sports clothing, film,
publishing, the arts, new media – often clients come
to us for a new creative direction, for a way of thinking,
this informs the visual work.

DC: TWO:design is a privately owned Limited company.
A lot of companies spend most of their time on non-
creative issues, like keeping their shareholders happy,
or acting as a small cog in a large design dinosaur
– we choose not to have those considerations. We
concentrate on making the best work we can.

GP: That's right! We are here to be creative, to solve
problems, to build brands. We keep our ears close to
the street, and our minds open...

UffindellWest

94

24 St John Street
London EC1M4AY
t: +44 (0)20 7689 0000
email: erika@uffindellwest.com
www.uffindellwest.com

Brand Strategy
Communications Consultancy
Brand Experience

UffindellWest is a leading consultancy with an
established reputation for contributing to major
national and international brands. We devise and
implement brand strategies through market mapping
and competitor reviews; provide communications
consultancy including 'Living the Brand' programmes:
and reinforce brand experience while enhancing your
Customer Relationship Management.

As part of our ability to strengthen your brand we have
an integral design arm, which not only creates fresh,
intelligent and effective solutions but establishes and
oversees worldwide brand management programmes
and communications projects.

So if you want to increase the equity in your brand and
add value to your business, talk to us. We specialise in
building performance into brands.

clients
APU Anglia Polytechnic University
BSI
BG Group
Biomni
Consignia
Corridor
Countryside Properties
Fastrade
Investors in People
Kingston Communications
Logica
Lombard
London Business School
Notting Hill Housing Trust
Parcelforce Worldwide
Quantum Exhibitions
Royal & SunAlliance
Sarasin Investments
Summit Hotels
Tertio
The Royal Bank of Scotland
Transport for London
Vickers Defence
William M.Mercer

See also section New Media Design p. 138

01

03

INVESTORS IN
PEOPLE UK

UNA (London)
Designers
Graphic Design

Management: Nick Bell
Contacts: Nick Bell
Staff: 5
Founded: 1988

5.5 Alaska 500 Building
61 Grange Road
London SE1 3BA
t: +44 (0)20 7394 8838/f: +44 (0)20 7394 8865
email: nickbell@unadesigners.co.uk

Company Profile

UNA's expertise spans both cultural and business
sectors. We carry out work for museums, art galleries,
record companies, publishers, educational
establishments, business organisations, cultural
institutions, local authorities and private companies.
Books, magazines, catalogues, brochures, corporate
identities, exhibitions, web sites and signage programmes are just some of the things we have designed
during fourteen years of practice.

Formerly known as Nick Bell Design. Became
associated with UNA of Amsterdam in 1998. In 1997
Nick Bell was appointed art director of Eye. Nick Bell
has lectured widely in the States and Europe and his
work has been published in design journals such as
Eye and most notably Emigre (No. 22 in 1992) when
the whole issue was devoted to his work and teaching.
"Bell's interest in the ambiguity and complexity of
language and imagery as iconic signifier is unusual in
its level of intelligence and articulacy". "Bell's spare
typography illustrates his refined understanding of
semantics" - Rick Poynor (from the "Lost and Found"
catalogue, Birkhauser/The British Council, 1999)

Clients

Tate Publishing, Tate Britain, Taschen, Phaidon Press,
The Science Museum, Virgin Classics, Barbican Centre,
Royal Mail, Hayward Gallery, Quantum Business Media,
Salamanca 2002, Mona Hatoum, John Lyall architects,
muf architecture/art, Casson Mann Designers.

1. Stills from a typographic installation debating the use of
nuclear fuel for generating electricity. On six 6x8m projection
screens, the largest av installation in the UK. Part of a
permanent exhibition at the BNFL Visitors Centre, Sellafield,
Cumbria. Commissioned and curated by the Science Museum,
London

2. Cover and spreads from Martin Parr, the first retrospective
of the British photographer's work. Written by Val Williams and
Published by Phaidon Press, 2002. UNA (London) designers
also designed the Martin Parr exhibition at the Barbican Gallery
in 2002, curated by Val Williams.

3. Tablecloth, 125x125 cm, designed for refectory tables 80x80
cm. Commissioned by the British Council to accompany and
record responses to "Lost and Found", an exhibition of British
design in Belgium, 1999. Inspired by the British landscape, it
shows the rivers that drain off England and Wales north, south,
east and west. Text from Jacquetta Hawkes's book, "A Land",
Cresset Press, 1951

4. Eye, the international review of graphic design. Cover and
spreads show the redesign. Nos 41 and 42 vol. 11, 2001.
Creative director Nick Bell.

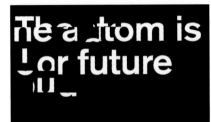

There is no country in the world that has found an acceptable solution for its radioactive waste

PEER DE RIJK, WISE (WORLD INFORMATION SERVICE ON ENERGY AND NUCLEAR INFORMATION), 2000/2001

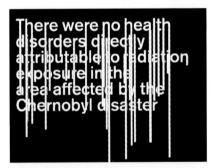

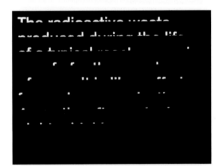

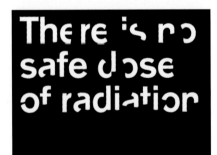

1

that still inhabits his work today. He was fascinated by the idea of preference and taste – what makes people choose each other, the idiosyncratic way in which domestic interiors are created, why we follow traditions when their original rationale has long since disappeared.

Twenty-seven years later, when he travelled around Britain in 1998 making a documentary film, he was like a stranger in a foreign land. A gang of girls in Newcastle, skittering along the seafront in a gale, accused him of being a trainspotter; a holidaymaker gave him a lecture about the evils of immigration and a homeowner expressed his sense of alienation from his birthplace. Perhaps the Newcastle girls were essentially right: he is always watching, taking in the detail, wandering around places where no one knows him, a collector of faces, gestures and social indiscretions.

Parr's photography is essentially a reflection of intense curiosity, deriving much from the American photography

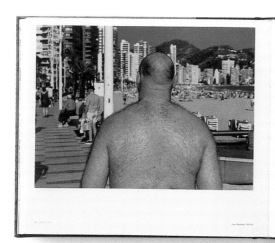

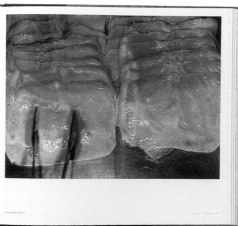

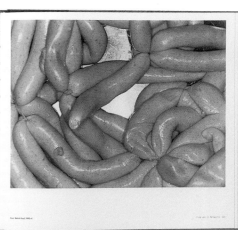

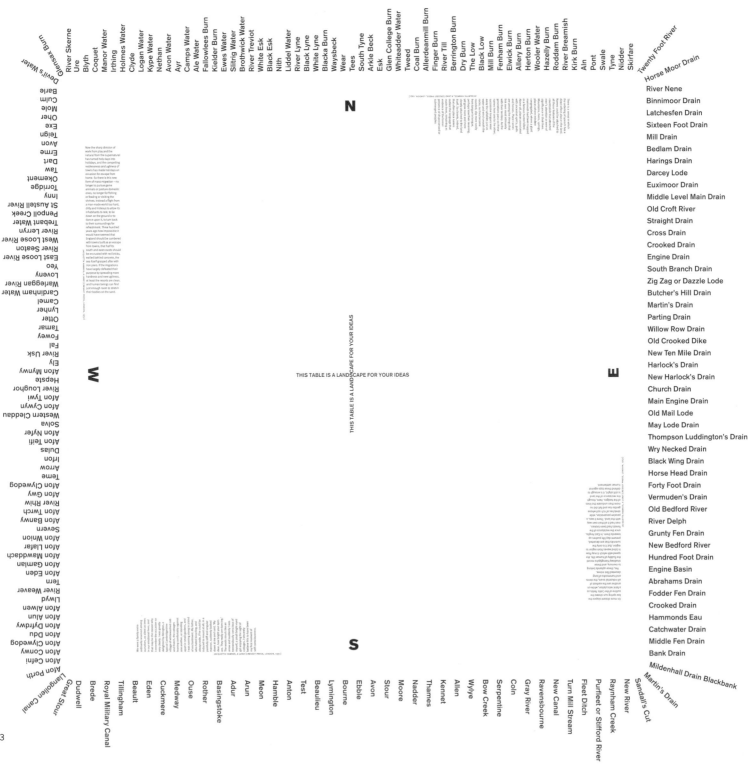

THIS TABLE IS A LANDSCAPE FOR YOUR IDEAS

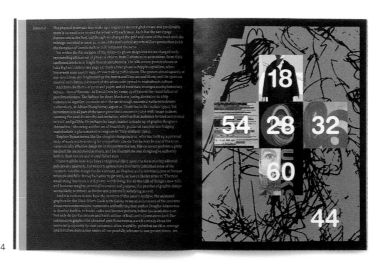

Wall Design and Art Direction

42 Kingsway Place
Sans Walk
London EC1R 0LU
t: +44 (0)20 7251 2004/f: +44 (0)20 7251 2095
m: +44 (0)7957 186 748
email: info@wallwideweb.com
www.wallwideweb.com

Founded in 2000, by Sheridan Wall, Wall Design & Art Direction produces multi-disciplined graphic design for numerous high-profile clients, as well as work for many individuals and smaller companies. Extensive industry expertise and experience enables us to offer clients a complete consultancy service. We consistently produce high-quality creative end products for a diverse client base. For our identity and branding packages, brochures, advertising campaigns, record and book covers, marketing and point of sale material, and web-based projects we employ a strong concept-based problem solving approach and attention to detail.

1658 Melrose Avenue
Los Angeles, Calif. USA

Star of Bengal
London, England

Empire State
New York, NY USA

42 Kingsway Place, Sans Walk
London, England

867 Pico Blvd.
Los Angeles, Calif. USA

Church of Religious Science
Los Angeles, Calif. USA

Flatiron Building
New York, NY USA

East 54th Street
New York, NY USA

Freemont Street
Las Vegas, Nevada, USA

Plaza de la Revolucion
Havana, Cuba

Algiers Hotel & Resort
Las Vegas, Nevada, USA

Ben & Jason
Record Cover & Campaign
GoBeat Records

Cyntra Place
Brochure, Logo & Advertising
C&A Donovan

Cyntra Place
Brochure Spread
C&A Donovan

Cyntra Place
Brochure Spread
C&A Donovan

Serpent's Tail
2001-2002 Brochure
Serpent's Tail Publishers

Photonica Discovery
Advertising
Photonica UK

Universe Works
Brochure, Logo & Advertising
Northill

Ben & Jason
Record Cover & Campaign
GoBeat Records

Toby Litt / Lester Bangs
Book Covers
Penguin / Serpent's Tail Publishers

Ocean of Sound / Walter Mosley
Book Covers
Serpent's Tail Publishers

Kamelian
Corporate Identity Package
Kamelian Ltd

Studio 2, Lower Ground Floor
42 Kingsway Place, Sans Walk
London EC1R 0LU

Tel: +44 (0)20 7251 2004
Fax: +44 (0)20 7251 2095
Mob: +44 (0)7957 186 748

ISDN: +44 (0)20 7251 2097
Email: info@wallwideweb.com
Web: www.wallwideweb.com

Zero 2 Firoco

Management: Paul Price
Contacts: Paul Price
Staff: 8
Founded: 1990

3 Bloomsbury Place
London WC1A 2QL
t: +44 (0)20 7436 9712/f: +44 (0)20 7436 9506
email: info@zero2firoco.com
www.zero2firoco.com

Zero 2 Firoco help businesses to develop their corporate image and visual communication. Our mission is to help you exceed in your industry through excellence in our own.

We offer an integrated set of services delivered in-house. Our services include communication planning, market positioning, corporate identity and brochure design, direct mail, advertising, exhibition and web site design.

We work with an exciting mix of clients ranging from major blue-chips to owner managed organisations. Working within a broad range of industry sectors and communicating with a wide range of target audiences has enabled us to keep our strategic thinking and creative solutions fresh and original.

Clients
Alcan Europe
BBC Education
BBC Radio One
BSkyB
Carlton Screen Advertising
Clear Channel
Disney Channel
Down's Syndrome Association
Euromonitor
Grant Thornton International
Health Education Authority
ICM Research
King Sturge
Leo House Partnership
Office Angels
M&C Saatchi/Morgan Stanley
Sandcliff
Taylor Nelson Sofres
Warner Home Video
Warner Vision UK
Weber Shandwick Worldwide

1. Corporate identity design, Sandcliff
2. Corporate identity update and worldwide implementation, Grant Thornton International
3. Naming, promotion identity and campaign, Morgan Stanley
4. Corporate identity, Hauck Research International
5-6. Promotion brochure and Election promotion brochure, BSkyB - Sky News
7. Packaging, Warner Home Video
8-9. Packaging and Advertising, Helkon SK/Warner Home Video
10. Corporate sales brochure, Office Angels
11-12. Corporate sales brochure and spread, Clear Channel
13-14. Sales brochure cover and spread, Alcan Europe

1

2

3

4

5

6

7

8

9

10

11

12

13

14

Zip Design & Art Direction

Management: Peter Chadwick
Contacts: Charlie Banks, Peter Chadwick
Staff: 6
Founded: 1996

Queen's Studio:
Unit 2A 121 Salusbury Rd
London NW6 6RG
t: +44 (0)20 7372 4474/f: +44 (0)20 7372 4484
email: charlie@zipdesign.co.uk
www.zipdesign.co.uk

Zip Design was formed in 1996, Peter Chadwick, its
director, has established a creative and innovative
team to champion new areas of graphic design as
well as web design. Zip Design has grown rapidly
and whose strengths combine creative flair and
unparalleled client focus, with street level cool and
a well developed sense of irony. Zip offers both original
and fresh design, alongside a comprehensive multimedia package that includes web design and broadcast / on-air graphics from sister companies
Lo-Fly and Punk.

Clients include
Bugged Out!
Cream
Cohn and Wolfe Advertising
East West Records
EMI Records
Harvey Nichols
Hed Kandi
Lee Cooper
MTV
Obsessive/BMG
Parlophone Records
Paul Smith
Swatch
Sony Music
Ultra Records USA
Wildstar Records

1-2. LP Cover and campaign image, Obsessive/BMG.
March 2002
3-5. Campaign, Skint Records. July to Nov 2001
6. Label identity, Skyline Records June 2001
7. Advertising Campaign, MTV. June 2001
8. LP Cover, Ideal . June 2001
9. LP Cover, Critical Mass. August 2001
10. LP Cover, Virgin. June . 1999
11. Press Invite, Lee Cooper. March 2002
12. LP Cover, Hed Kandi. February 2002
13. Logo identites, Stereo Sushi. January 2002
14. Inner Sleeve, Outcaste. June 2001
15. LP cover, Outcaste. December 2000
16. LP Cover, Union Square Music. January 2002
17. Advertising, Scala. March - July 2001
18. Advertising, Bugged Out! at Cream. August 2001 to
present
19. Poster for LP release, Southern Fried Records. January
2002
20-24. Campaign, Jive Pepper. April - October 1999

1

Felix da Housecat
Excursions

2

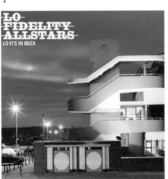

3

4

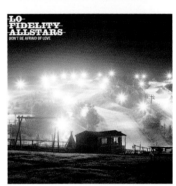

5

6

7

9

New Wave
Home Entertainment

8

10

11

12

13

14

GROOVE ARMADA

If Everybody Looked The Same

20

FATBOY SLIM

LIVE ON BRIGHTON BEACH

19

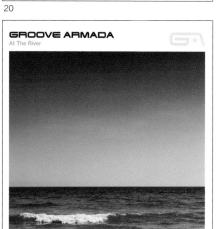

GROOVE ARMADA

At The River

21

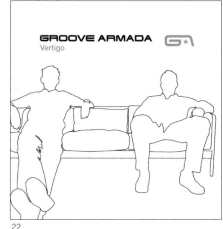

GROOVE ARMADA

Vertigo

22

15

HARLEM
SESSIONS

16

18

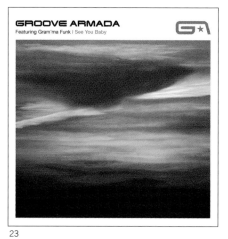

GROOVE ARMADA

Featuring Gram'ma Funk I See You Baby

23

GROOVE ARMADA

The Remixes

24

17

Zynk Design Consultants

Management: Clinton Pritchard, Stavros Theodoulou
Staff: 4

10 The Chandlery
50 Westminster Bridge Road
London SE1 7QY
t: +44 (0)20 7721 7444/f: +44 (0)20 7721 7443
email: info@zynkdesign.com
www.zynkdesign.com

Zynk design consultants were formed in the spring of 1998 by Clinton Pritchard and Stavros Theodoulou, managing partners. With extensive experience in the retail, corporate, hospitality and health and fitness market sectors, we offer an extended level of graphic and interior design consultancy services, focusing on the development of branded environments.

From initial concept to project completion, all clients are assigned a managing partner responsible for the delivery of the clients objectives. Often these are unclear or unknown at the outset and using our skills and experience as commercial branding designers, we initiate a dialogue that allows us to get 'under the skin' of an organisation, or operation and assess the strategic needs and commercial objectives that are desired or required.

Our experience has led us to best describe our complimentary skills as those of 'Brand Evolutionists'.

See also volume Interior, Retail and Event Design p. 66

Workout ~ Relax ~ You choose

ISOSPA - Local Authority Health & Fitness Centres
CLIENT: SERCO
PROJECT: Interior Design, Implementation, Brand Identity, Environmental Graphics, Signage, Stationery, Marketing Literature.

club
indigo
fitness | health | life

CLUB INDIGO - Private Health & Fitness Club Chain
CLIENT: INVICTA LEISURE

PROJECT: Interior Design, Implementation, Brand Identity, Environmental Graphics, Signage, Stationery, Marketing Literature.

AVANTI - Birmingham University
Campus - Campus
CLIENT: BIRMINGHAM
UNIVERSITY
PROJECT: Interior Design,
Implementation, Brand Identity,
Environmental Graphics, Signage.

EITEM - Management Consultancy
Office Design
CLIENT: ETIEM
PROJECT: Interior Design,
Implementation, Signage.

GO - Birmingham University
Campus - Café
CLIENT: BIRMINGHAM
UNIVERSITY
PROJECT: Interior Design,
Implementation, Brand Identity,
Environmental Graphics, Signage.

brand evolutionists...

zynk ^(Zn)

UNIVERSAL - London Head Office
- Corporate & Social Spaces.
CLIENT: UNIVERSAL MUSIC
INTERNATIONAL
PROJECT: Interior Design,
Implementation, Environmental
Graphics.

ONE NEW INN SQUARE INN -
Private Dinning Rooms &
Residence
CLIENT: DAVID VANDERHOOK
PROJECT: Interior Design,
Implementation, Lighting Design,
Soft Furnishings.

LIME ⊘

LIME - Bar & Restaurant
CLIENT: LIME ENTERTAINMENTS
LTD.
PROJECT: Interior Design,
Implementation, Brand Identity,
Environmental Graphics, Menu's,
Marketing Literature.

New Media Design

Central Industrial
The future is this way

Management: Mr D A Carry, Mr P A Carry
Contacts: Dave
Staff: 10
Founded: 2001

60 Poland Street
Soho
London W1F 7NT
t: +44 (0)20 7287 6544/f: +44 (0)20 7287 6554
email: enquiries@central-industrial.co.uk
www.thefutureisthisway.com

Company profile

Central Industrial was founded by David Carry (Creative Architect) and Paul Carry (Creative Director) in 2001. The vision was to create a new breed of hypermedia design consultancy; one that combines solid graphic and interface solutions with a strong focus on user experience, information architecture, and strategy based on real-world experience and research.

The Carry brothers' design partnership, that has spanned some 12 years, combines contemporary graphic, 3d and motion design with a significant understanding of human-computer interaction and online branding.

Clients:
Associated New Media
Avocent
BBC
CenterParcs
CitiBank
Clear Channel Entertainment
Codemasters
Coral Eurobet
Datatec
Deutsche Bank
Discovery Networks Europe
Disney
Euro RSCG
Hewlett Packard
Logical Group
Novartis
One 2 One
Proctor & Gamble
Racal
Raytheon
Thomson
Warner Bros
Vizzavi

CENTRAL INDUSTRIAL

HYPERMEDIA // DESIGN // FILM & VIDEO PRODUCTION
// AUDIO // STRATEGY // **THE FUTURE IS THIS WAY**

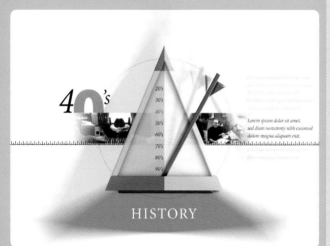

Grahams Hi Fi
Sales Tool // CD ROM

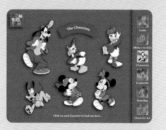

Disney
Mickey for Kids // CD ROM

Digital Travel Group
Shortbreaks // Website

CENTRAL INDUSTRIAL

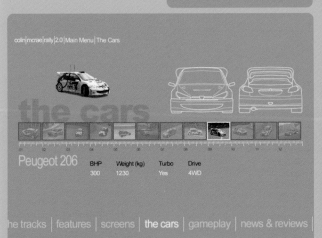

Codemasters

Colin McRae Rally 2.0
// Flash Website

Warner Music

The Corrs // Website

Centerparcs

Booking // Website

Datatec

PowerTools // CDROM

Novartis

Nicotinell // Website

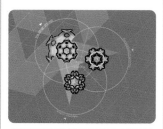

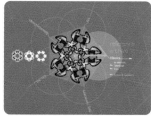

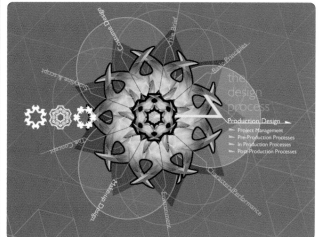

BBC
Visions // Broadband

Logical
Global B2B // Website

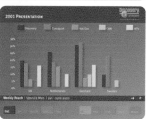

Discovery
Ad Sales // DVD ROM

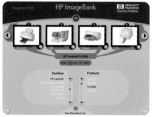

Hewlett Packard
Imagebank // CD ROM

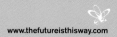

www.thefutureisthisway.com

Design Bridge
Digital Media

Management: Sir William Goodenough, Assaf Guery
Contacts: Assaf Guery
Staff: 10
Founded: 2001

London office
18 Clerkenwell Close
London EC1R 0QN
t: +44 (0)20 7814 9922/f: +44 (0)20 7814 9024
email: assaf.guery@designbridge.co.uk
www.designbridge.co.uk

Amsterdam office
Keizersgracht 424
1016 GC Amsterdam
Netherlands
t: +31 (0)20 520 6030/f: +31 (0)20 520 6059
email: marian@designbridge.nl
www.designbridge.co.uk

At Design Bridge we believe that brands are like
people. They come in all shapes and sizes, from the
well-adjusted to those with more deep-rooted
problems and still more just waiting to be born.
Whatever the scenario, we speak their language and
understand their needs. The common thread is
always fresh thinking, with every brief a new challenge.

Our particular strategic and creative skills can be used
individually, or in combination, to unlock the potential
in every brand. Whether the most compelling need is
for a new corporate or brand identity, promotional
literature, a three-dimensional expression of a brand,
bespoke bottle or graphic packaging, or even a digital
media campaign, we have over 15 years' experience
helping companies around the world to realise their
goals, and those of their product or service brands.

Digital Media is a fundamentally important part of the
brand landscape. It is the only medium that
guarantees a two-way dialogue with customers and
within an organisation. Recognising this, though, is not
enough - to maintain 'share of mind', brands need to
find innovative new ways of reaching out. This means
using the most appropriate digital channels - PDA,
Internet, interactive TV, CD rom or DVD - to promote
your brand in the right way to the right audience.

See also section Branding and Graphic Design p. 20
See also volume Product and Packaging Design p. 36

1. Munchsters: a true eatertainment brand,
www.munchsters.com brings it to life
2. AEP: a changed tone of voice allows American Electric
Power to reach a new European audience
3. Clearspace: for this data hosting start-up,
www.clearspace.com is the primary sales tool
4. Easybroker: usability was paramount for this new global
on-line share trading company
5. MakingMusic.org.uk: warm, exciting and inclusive, the
new website provides members with services from the UK's
largest Art Organisation

DESIGN BRIDGE

Imagination

25 Store Street
South Crescent
London WC1E 7BL
t: +44 (0)20 7323 3300
email: questions@imagination.com
www.imagination.com

Imagination

"The range of Imagination's work stretches
conventional definitions of design" Stephen Bayley

"Imagination is an ideas company. If there's a
hierarchy, it's creativity before execution. That's one
of the reasons I enjoy going there - because I feel
stimulated creatively."
J Mays, Vice President, Design, Ford Motor Company

Imagination has worked with the world's leading
brands for over 25 years to become a global agency
with offices in London, New York, Detroit, Hong Kong,
Tokyo and Stockholm. It has a culture as distinctive as
its name. The quality of its people, the integrity of its
thought and its uncompromising commitment to
creativity, ultimately defines its approach.

Imagination pioneered the idea of brand experience.
That is, not just what a brand communicates in two
dimensions, but the emotions, feelings and responses
it can arouse in all dimensions. It has achieved this
through its unique multi-disciplinary offer, employing
architects, interior designers, graphic designers,
writers, film makers, photographers, lighting and
multimedia experts, all under one roof.

Imagination's multimedia team co-ordinates a wealth
of creative and technical expertise to create a diverse
mix of audio visual media. It integrates both digital and
traditional methods to deliver captivating interactive
creativity. From linear animation to 3D virtual games,
Imagination's innovative work spans interactives,
motion graphics, web creation, gaming and pioneering
immersive environments.

See also section Branding and Graphic Design p. 38
See also volume Interior, Retail and Event Design p. 38

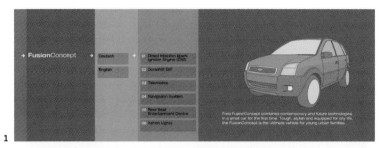

1

2

3

4

1-4. Touch screen interactive, Ford Fusion Concept, Frankfurt
Motor Show, September 2001.
5-7. Touch screen interactive, Aston Martin V12 Vanquish,
Geneva Motor Show,
March 2001.
8-10. The Guinness Storehouse experience on-line, launched
November 2000. www.guinnessstorehouse.com

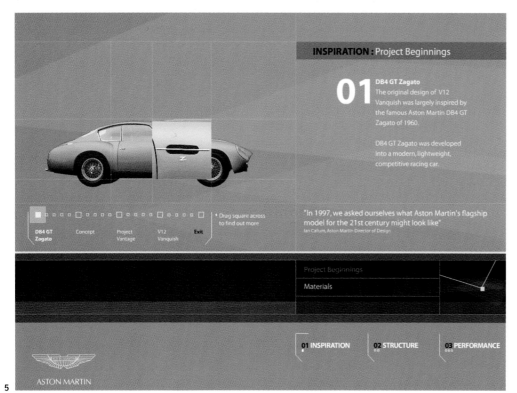

INSPIRATION : Project Beginnings

01 DB4 GT Zagato

The original design of V12 Vanquish was largely inspired by the famous Aston Martin DB4 GT Zagato of 1960.

DB4 GT Zagato was developed into a modern, lightweight, competitive racing car.

DB4 GT Zagato · Concept · Project Vantage · V12 Vanquish · Exit

Drag square across to find out more

"In 1997, we asked ourselves what Aston Martin's flagship model for the 21st century might look like"
Ian Callum, Aston Martin Director of Design

Project Beginnings

Materials

01 INSPIRATION · **02 STRUCTURE** · **03 PERFORMANCE**

ASTON MARTIN

5

6

7

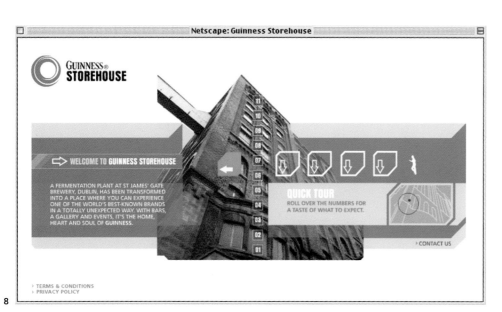

8

9

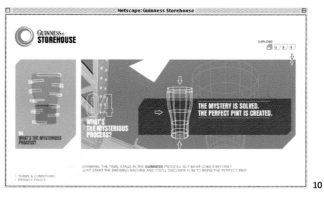

10

Oakwood dc
Stategic integrated design

Management: Phil Marshall / Neil Sims / Chris Jones
Contacts: Phil Marshall / Chris Jones
Staff: 42
Founded: 1995
Memberships: British Design Initiative / Institute of Directors

7 Park Street
Bristol BS1 5NF
t: +44 (0)11 7983 6789/f: +44 (0)11 7983 7323
email: user@oakwood-dc.com
www.oakwood-dc.com

Company profile

Oakwood dc was founded by three partners who shared the vision of ensuring their clients' commercial success by consistently delivering creative and impactful design, combined with a high quality cost service. From this beginning in 1995, Oakwood dc has grown into a strategic design consultancy that spans three inter-related disciplines:

Oakwood sd specialises in strategic graphic design from corporate identity, branding and literature through to packaging and direct mail. Oakwood 3d concentrates on designing and building the structures that make up creative retail and leisure environments, while Oakwood idc works exclusively with screen-based media to create dynamic websites, database-driven applications, CD-Rom presentations and interactive animations.

The strength of Oakwood dc is its team of individual characters and personalities, with diverse backgrounds and experiences. Our talented team works hand-in-hand with company professionals from various industries to ensure that the commercial relationship between the product or brand and the creative design is guaranteed.

See also section Branding and Graphic Design p. 52
See also volume Interior, Retail and Event Design p. 46

1. Interactive packaging style guide (dual platform).

Management: Mike Horseman (Managing Director),
Gary Cooke (Creative Director)
Contacts: Mike Horseman and Robert Hall
Staff: 22
Founded: 1983
Memberships: D&AD, DBA, RSA

Mill House:
8 Mill Street
London SE1 2BA
t: +44 (0)20 7740 7000/f: +44 (0)20 7740 7001
email: robert.hall@openagency.com
www.openagency.com

The Open Agency is a design company specialising
in New Media, Packaging, Brand Identity and
Literature. Our ability to comprehend what needs to
be communicated is coupled with our inventiveness
- ultimately resulting in a strong and original concept.

We believe that informality and openness isn't
contradictory to good business, and ensures our full
understanding of our customers' requirements. By
being open and honest, with both our clients and
ourselves, we have developed a working environment
that is fun, yet commercial. Only by being truly open
and approachable do we best represent our clients'
interests.

See also section Branding and Graphic Design p. 54

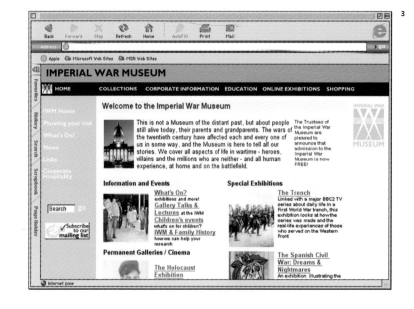

1. GKN
www.gknplc.co.uk
2. South West Trains
www.swtrains.co.uk
3. Imperial War Museum
www.iwm.org.uk
4. Dan Dare
www.dandare.com

Renfrew Creative

Contacts: *Bruce Renfrew*
Staff: *42*
Founded: *1982*

Rocket Studios
Abbey Meadow
Leicester LE4 5DF
t: +44 (0)116 2531 961/f: +44 (0)116 2539 827
email: br@rg3.com
www.rg3.com

Profile

DesignIT, part of Renfrew Creative, helps build
relationships between the consumer and the brand,
bringing brand values to life. Through a combination
of creative vision, technical innovation and exceptional
digital media skills, DesignIT provides its clients with
new and effective solutions to the communication
challenge.

Clients include

Ford Rally Sport
Microsens Technologies
Bam Entertainment
Sony Playstation
Advantica
Medic Group Inc
Swinton Insurance
Namco
Bounty SA
Brent Electronics

See also volume Product and Packaging Design p. 26

designIT

Showreel 2002 / frames 00:00:00:00 - 00:03:04:00 / the story so far.

designIT
www.designit.co.uk

designIT
www.designit.co.uk

designIT
www.designit.co.uk

designIT
www.designit.co.uk

designIT
www.designit.co.uk

00:03:04:00

Rufus Leonard

Management: Neil Svensen, Principal Director;
Steve Howell, Executive Creative Director;
Susan Costello, Director of Technology Innovations;
Todd Brown, IT Solutions Director
Contacts: Zoe Shortis
Staff: 100
Founded: 1989
Memberships: British Interactive Media Association

The Drill Hall
57a Farringdon Road
London EC1M 3JB
t: +44 (0)20 7404 4490/f: +44 (0)20 7404 4491
email: newbusiness@rufusleonard.com
www.rufusleonard.com

Since its foundation in 1989, Rufus Leonard has
become one of the UK's leading brand and digital
business consultancies.

We combine great marketing ideas and technology
in the space where organisations must be more
effective than ever: in the ways they communicate
with customers, or stakeholders, and in the flow of
information between these groups.

Digital media work interactively in this flow, and in
this flow brand comes alive.

Ideas \ Brand \ Technology

See also section Branding and Graphic Design p. 66

Ideas Technology Brand

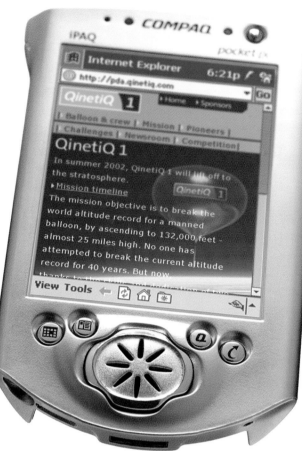

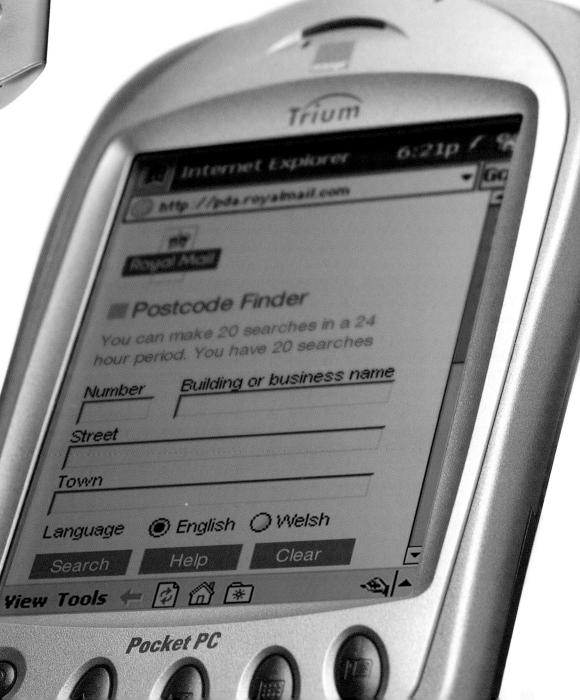

Saatchi & Saatchi Design

Management: Simon Steel - Managing Director, Debbie Orrell - Client Services Director, Iain Ross - Design Director, Ian Lanksbury - Design Director
Contacts: Simon Steel, Debbie Orrell
Staff: 25

89 Whitfield Street
London W1T 4HG
t: +44 (0)20 7307 5327/f: +44 (0)20 7307 5328
email: ssteel@saatchi-design.com
www.saatchi-design.com

Company profile

Saatchi & Saatchi Design is part of TfG, the biggest on-site production unit in Europe. We provide creative solutions and integrated resources for brand positioning, naming, corporate and brand identity, interactive media and broadcast design.

Clients

Aspective - Corporate identity/literature
BBC - Programme identity
Bulmers - Annual report & accounts
Camelot - Corporate identity/literature
CCSD/Fuel - Corporate identity
Comic Relief - Fundraising literature
Crone Corkill - Literature & website
Energy Savings Trust/Future Energy - identity/literature
Hampstead Theatre - Branding/literature
Hewlett Packard - Branding
3i - Literature
KPMG - Branding
LIFFE - Product marketing, branding and annual report & accounts
Linklaters & Alliance - Corporate identity/literature
Metropolitan Police - Divisional identity
National Lottery - Corporate identity/branding/POS/literature
Premier Oil - Annual report & accounts/literature/website
PPG Autocolor - Global press advertising
Schroders - Annual report & accounts
Toyota Europe - Brand Identity/Pan-European literature system
Visa - Brand positioning for Europe & CEMEA regions

See also section Branding and Graphic Design p. 68

1

DISCOVER

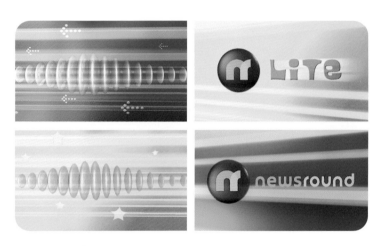

2

CREATE

3

1. BBC - The Saturday Show identity, brand personality and language, title sequence, stings, interclips and live action.
2. BBC - Newsround identity and title sequence. We defined a unique positioning, brand personality, environment and complete identity package
3. Selection of new media and interactive projects for Liffe, Tilt, Crone Corkill and Shell Like

   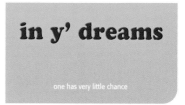

PERCEIVE   CHALLENGE

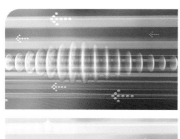   

  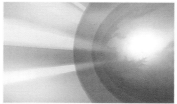 

ENJOY   SMILE

 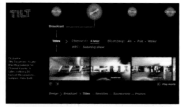 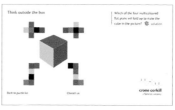 

SAATCHI & SAATCHI
DESIGN

Sears Davies

Corporate identity, corporate literature and digital design

Management: Julian Davies, Stewart Webber, Ben Tobin, Craig Stafford
Contacts: Julian Davies
Staff: 16
Founded: 1988
Memberships: CSD

25A Copperfield Street
London SE1 0EN
t: +44 (0)20 7633 0939/f: +44 (0)20 7633 9953
email: info@searsdavies.com
www.searsdavies.com

A unique combination of design talent and strategic thinking has enabled Sears Davies to establish an enviable position within the corporate communications sector. Through listening to our clients' objectives and sharing ideas, we help them to achieve commercial success by delivering inspirational and effective design solutions.

Active in all areas of graphic design, we continue to demonstrate our skills in the creation of corporate identity and branding, company literature and annual reports, digital design, promotional campaigns and direct mail initiatives for an enviable portfolio of clients.

Clients
Allsport
Associated Capital Theatres
British Gas
Charnos plc
CIS Insurance
Crown Office Chambers
Dar Al-Handasah (Shair and Partners)
Department of Trade & Industry
Eastern Electricity plc
Export Credits Guarantee Department
Foreign & Commonwealth Office
Generali SpA
Greenland Interactive
Heath Lambert Group
Highways Agency
Imperial College
Leo Burnett
Lloyds TSB Group Union
London Electricity plc
London Transport Buses
Macfarlanes
Macmillan Cancer Relief Fund
Matrix Securities
Memery Crystal
Merrill Lynch Investment Managers
Museum of Garden History
Natural History Museum
One Essex Court
Pantaenius
Property Bar Association
Simon Petroleum Technology
Speciality Retail Group
Welsh Rugby Union

See also section Branding and Graphic Design p. 70

128

enter >

1	2	3
4	5	6

1 **www.dargroup.com**
Consulting Engineers

2 **www.macfarlanes.com**
Solicitors

3 **Highways Agency**
Interactive CD ROM

4 **www.greenland.co.uk**
Response Management

5 **Foreign & Commonweath Office**
Interactive CD ROM

6 **www.heathlambert.com**
Insurance Brokers

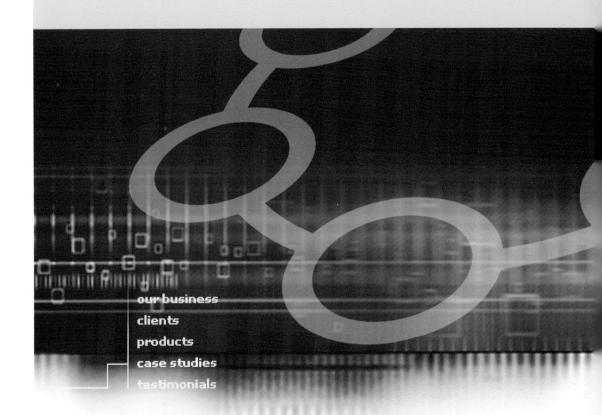

our business
clients
products
case studies
testimonials

identities & brands | literature | promotional campaigns | retail graphics | digital design

searsdaviesdesigners

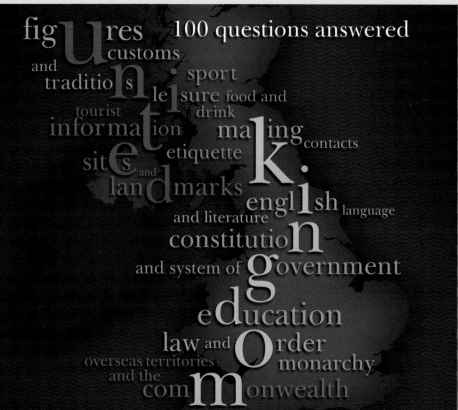

100 questions answered

figures
and
customs
traditions
sport
leisure
tourist
food and
drink
information
making
sites
etiquette
contacts
and
landmarks
english language
and literature
constitution
and system of government
education
law and Order
monarchy
overseas territories
and the
commonwealth

united kingdom

Sharpedge
Design and
Communication

Management: Diana Inglis and Lloyd Clater
Contacts: Diana Inglis, Lloyd Clater
Founded: 1992

1 Silex Street
LONDON SE1 0DP
t: +44 (0)20 7633 0003/f: +44 (0)20 7633 0020
email: contact@sharpedge.co.uk
www.sharpedge.co.uk

10 years of effective solutions

Sharpedge Design and Communication was
established in 1992 and celebrated ten successful
years in April 2002.

The consultancy works closely with clients to develop
ideas that meet the aims and objectives of any project.
Our work is identifiable by its combination of function
and craftsmanship, combined with a deep understanding of design and marketing and the role they
play in successful business ventures.

Our field is graphic design and new media and
Sharpedge has been involved with several major
advertising campaigns, land regeneration projects,
corporate identities, promotional material, on-line
communications, video production and various 3D
installations for many large organisations.

Sharpedge is committed to working closely with
clients to provide award-winning design and effective
marketing strategies, that are on time and within
budget.

See also section Branding and Graphic Design p. 72

File   Edit   View   Special   Help

HEATHROW AIRPORT >> 25 MINUTES BY ROAD

MARYLEBONE VILLAGE.COM
LONDON W1

HEATHROW AIRPORT >> 35 MINUTES

eat & drink

PICCADILLY CIRCUS >> 5 MINUTES

#107/108

IT TELECOMS >> HI-TECH INFRASTRUCTURE

well
connected
tranquil

residential

HAMMERSMITH EMBANKMENT

Color Gas Village of the Year

village of the year

calendar

active villages

eNewsletter

Welcome

ISLINGTON

how to use this section

ISLINGTON

getting the most from your course

ISLINGTON

your course - your future

ISLINGTON

92
93
94
95
96
97
98
99
00
01
02

ten years of effective solutions

Start Design Ltd
Brand identity, Interactive media, Marketing communication

Management: Mike Curtis and Darren Whittingham
Contacts: Mike Curtis and Darren Whittingham
Staff: 55
Founded: 1996
Memberships: DMA, Trust UK, CIM, DP Data Protection, Design Business Association, SPCA, British Design Initiative

Kingsbourne House
229-231 High Holborn
London WC1V 7DA
t: +44 (0)20 7269 0101/f: +44 (0)20 7269 0102
email: mike@startdesign.com
www.startdesign.com

Profile

Start Design gets results. Specialising in brand identity, interactive media and marketing communications, the agency develops award-winning solutions by placing the emphasis on strategy and ideas. Its creativity is driven by the needs of customers and the objectives of clients. Working with major UK and international organisations, Start has the design, copywriting and project management expertise to deliver complete solutions across all media.

Clients

Avis
COI Communications
Consignia
Eurobell/Telewest
Flextech Television
Home Office
Land Registry
Ordnance Survey
Parcel Force
Post Office
Royal Mail
thetrainline
The Times
Virgin Atlantic
Virgin Books
Virgin.com
Virgin Holidays
Virgin Management Ltd
Virgin Mobile
Virgin Money
Virgin One Account
Virgin V.Shop
Virgin Wines
Xchanging
Wolseley

See also section Branding and Graphic Design p. 76

1

2

www.iflyvirginatlantic.com

3

1. Interactive TV advertisement, Virgin Mobile, 2001
2. i-fly site for frequent flyers, Virgin Atlantic, 2002
3. In-store kiosk interface design, Virgin V.Shop, 2001
4. Site design, thetrainline, 2002
5. International Services site design, Royal Mail, 2002
6. Site design, Avis, 2000

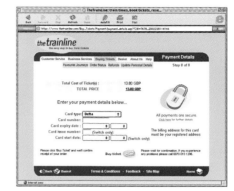

4

www.thetrainline.com

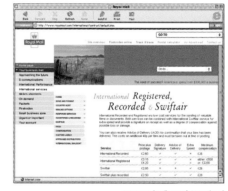

5

www.royalmail.com/international

6

www.avis.co.uk

Management: Jonathan Taylor-Horne
Contacts: Gordon Druce and Daisy Zudyk
Staff: 10
Founded: 1997

134 | Subliminal

4 Chapel Row
Queens Square
Bath BA1 1HN
t: +44 (0)1225 401 333/f: +44 (0)1225 402 031
email: info@subliminal.co.uk
www.subliminal.co.uk

Company profile

Subliminal is a multi-disciplinary creative agency whose
work is built upon solid concepts; creative and
conceptual thinking always to the fore. Subliminal
continually cast aside convention to deliver new kinds
of visual communication, with the teams' experience
covering: art direction, 2D/3D design, film and
photography, illustration, copywriting and interactive
design comprising: websites, CD-ROM/DVD production,
animation and sound design.

Stimulate. Communicate. Innovate.

Expertise

Interactive Design. Moving Image.

Clients include

3DO
Bastion PR
Blue Marlin
Channel 4
Future Publishing
Granada Television
ITV
Ourprice
PSM2 Magazine
Scot-Baker Agency
Sony Computer Entertainment Europe
Virgin Stores
Yorkshire Television

See also section Branding and Graphic Design p. 82

▲ IMAGE01. ABOVE. VIEW FROM LEFT TO RIGHT
01 'WWW.THESHOWWITHNONAME.CO.UK' WEBSITE / UNIVERSITY OF SOUTH WEST ENGLAND
02 WWW.BLUEMARLIN.CO.UK / WWW.SCOT-BAKER.COM / WWW.HCGWORLDWIDE.COM
03 'JONNY MOSELEY MAD TRIX' WEBSITE / 3DOEUROPE   04 'PSM2' COVER DVD / FUTURE PUBLISHING
05 'VIVA LA DIVA' TITLES / CHANNEL 4   06 COMPANY WEBSITE / SUBLIMINAL DESIGN

OR
CS' PAGE

PSM2 DVD
| AVAILABLE MONTHLY
| SEE LOCAL NEWSAGENT

MAILER DVD-ROM
| AVAILABLE SOON
| PLEASE ENQUIRE

WEBSITE
| AVAILABLE NOW
| WWW.SUBLIMINAL.CO.UK

SUBLIMINAL UPPER FLOOR / LEVEL 03 / SCREEN
SUBLIMINAL SCREEN COLOUR REFERENCE:
HTML: F67B0A / RGB: 246/123/10

▼ IMAGE02. BELOW. VIEW FROM LEFT TO RIGHT. TOP THEN BOTTOM
01, 11, 14 & 15 'PSM2' COVER DVD / FUTURE PUBLISHING   02 & 05 'VIVA LA DIVA' TITLES / CHANNEL 4
03, 06, 09 & 13 'JONNY MOSELEY MAD TRIX' WEBSITE / 3DO EUROPE
04 & 10 'THE SHOW WITH NO NAME' WEBSITE / UNIVERSITY OF SOUTH WEST ENGLAND
07, 08 & 12 COMPANY WEBSITE / SCOT-BAKER AGENCY

Tribal DDB
Interactive
Agency

Management: Alison Parker, Jane Cunningham
Contacts: Lee Wright Staff: 49
Founded: 1995
Memberships: D&AD

12 Bishops Bridge Road
Paddington
London W2 6AA
t: +44 (0) 20 7262 0011
email: info@tribalDDB.co.uk
www.tribalDDB.co.uk

Company profile

Tribal DDB is a top ten international digital marketing
agency, with a strong reputation for strategic thinking
and excellent creative work. Tribal DDB delivers the
full spectrum of digital services from online marketing,
media buying and planning and strategic direction
through to web design and programming.

The agency culture champions both the collaboration
between digital skills and the integration of interactive
projects with other communications. By actively
developing centres of excellence in design, online
marketing and creative thinking, Tribal DDB is able
to recommend across the full spectrum of interactive
disciplines and platforms to meet business needs
effectively and cost efficiently.

Tribal DDB has offices in 23 countries across Europe,
North America, Canada and Australasia.

Clients
AXA Insurance
British Bakeries
British Gas
British Tourist Authority
Camelot
EMAP
Guardian
Investia
Nationwide
OMD Europe
Shopsmart
Sony UK
Sports.com
Reuters
Roof Gardens
The Dairy Council
The Meat and Livestock Commission
Unilever Bestfoods
Volkswagen

1. "Searching for beauty in a dirty digital world."
A series of 26 icons for www.megastar.co.uk 2002

There are 26 letters in the alphabet which we learn from an
early age to recognise in an infinite variety of forms. They have
been inscribed by monks, generated by computers, scratched
in stone and waved on flags. So why do we bother to spend so
many hours inventing new icons?

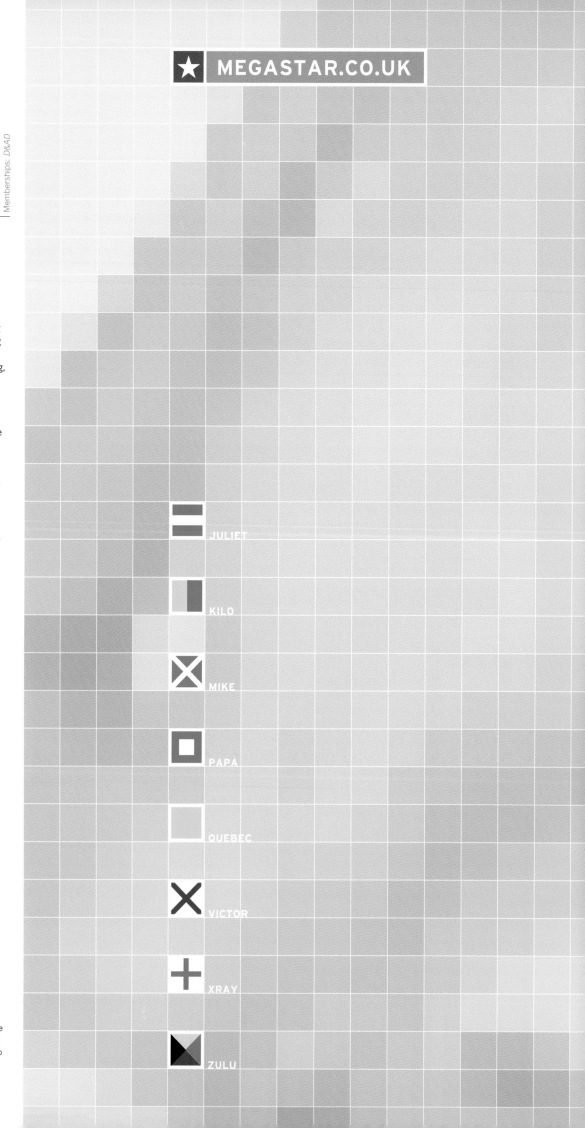

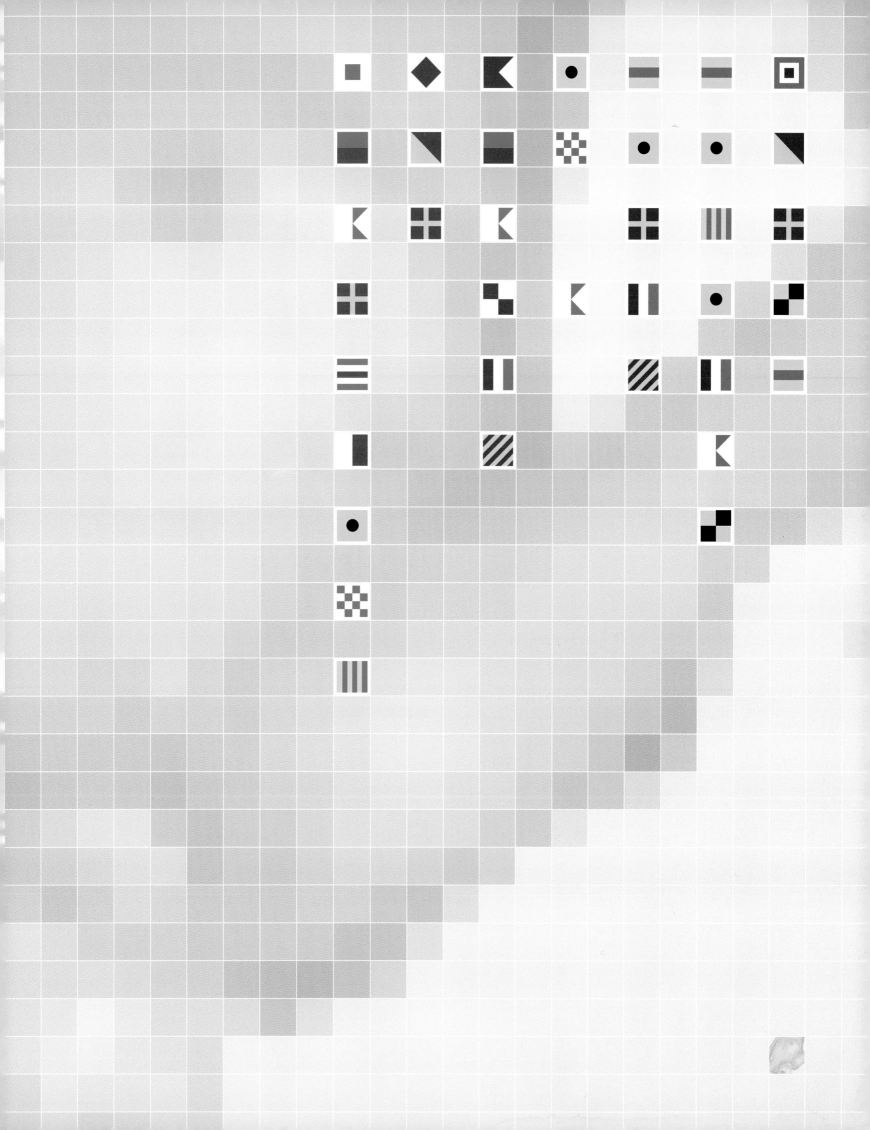

01

UffindellWest

138

24 St John Street
London EC1M4AY
t: +44 (0)20 7689 0000
email: erika@uffindellwest.com
www.uffindellwest.com

Brand Strategy
Communications Consultancy
Brand Experience

UffindellWest is a leading consultancy with an
established reputation for contributing to major
national and international brands. We devise and
implement brand strategies through market mapping
and competitor reviews; provide communications
consultancy including 'Living the Brand' programmes:
and reinforce brand experience while enhancing your
Customer Relationship Management.

As part of our ability to strengthen your brand we have
an integral design arm, which not only creates fresh,
intelligent and effective solutions but establishes and
oversees worldwide brand management programmes
and communications projects.

So if you want to increase the equity in your brand and
add value to your business, talk to us. We specialise in
building performance into brands.

clients
APU Anglia Polytechnic University
BSI
BG Group
Biomni
Consignia
Corridor
Countryside Properties
Fastrade
Investors in People
Kingston Communications
Logica
Lombard
London Business School
Notting Hill Housing Trust
Parcelforce Worldwide
Quantum Exhibitions
Royal & SunAlliance
Sarasin Investments
Summit Hotels
Tertio
The Royal Bank of Scotland
Transport for London
Vickers Defence
William M.Mercer

See also section Branding and Graphic Design p. 94

03

INVESTORS IN
PEOPLE UK

biomni ™

Advertisements

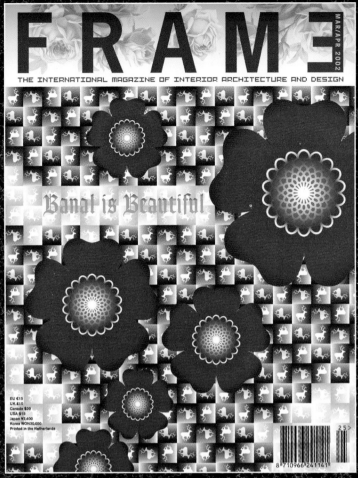

British Design Initiative

the focal point of british design

CORPORATE REGISTRATION   DESIGN INDUSTRY SURVEY   DESIGN NEWS SERVICE   DESIGN HANDBOOK 2003   DESIGN EXPORTS   DESIGN DIRECTORY   DESIGN ADVISORY SERVICE   DESIGN EVENTS

The British Design Initiative is an internationally recognised agency that provides a focal point for British design.

Established since 1993, it has built strong and trusted relationships with the UK's leading design agencies and with official design bodies, government and key media. Increasingly the British Design Initiative is working with those brand owners who strategically seek to align themselves with the design profession or provide products and services to the professions.

The BDI owns an accurate database of UK design agencies; design media, design awards and professional design bodies internationally. It currently has direct access to an estimated 85% of the entire UK market.

http://www.britishdesign.co.uk

The British Design Initiative, PO Box 34973, London SW6 6WB, Tel: +44 (0) 20 7384 3435, Fax: +44 (0) 20 7371 5343, E: info@britishdesign.co.uk

CHOICE™

A carnival of creative imagery for download

CUBA